Environmental pollution

Ian Foster

OXFORD UNIVERSITY PRESS

ACKNOWLEDGEMENTS

The publishers and author would like to thank the following people for their permission to use copyright material:

p.4 *top* Phil Brown, The Environmental Picture Library, *bottom* Don Hinrichsen, ICCE Photolibrary; p.11 *top* Dr Anne Smith, Science Photo Library, *bottom* Biophoto Associates; p.13 Robert Brook, The Environmental Picture Library; p.17 Heidi Bradner, The Environmental Picture Library; p.20 Patrick Sutherland, The Environmental Picture Library; p.36 Popperfoto/Reuter; p.41 V. Miles, The Environmental Picture Library.

The cover photograph is reproduced by permission of Morgan, Greenpeace.

Illustrations are by Herb Bowes Graphics, Oxford.

Every effort has been made to trace and contact copyright holders, but this has not always been possible. We apologise for any infringement of copyright.

Oxford University Press, Walton Street, Oxford OX2 6DP

Oxford New York Toronto Delhi Bombay Calcutta Madras Karachi Kuala Lumpur Singapore Hong Kong Tokyo Nairobi Dar es Salaam Cape Town Melbourne Auckland Madrid and associated companies in Berlin Ibadan

Oxford is a trade mark of Oxford University Press

© Oxford University Press 1991
First published 1991
Reprinted 1993

ISBN 0 19 913368 9

Typeset by Gem Publishing Company, Wallingford
Design and artwork by Herb Bowes Graphics, Oxford
Printed in Great Britain by
M & A Thomson Litho Ltd., East Kilbride, Scotland

PREFACE

Contemporary Issues in Geography is a series of books dealing with issues of concern to today's society. The series was developed as a result of our own teaching needs, especially when preparing INSET courses for teachers in Coventry and Warwickshire.

Hugh Matthews and Ian Foster, Series Editors

This book

Environmental Pollution has been written for advanced level students of geography and environmental science. The intention of this book is to provide a sound background to pollution problems, their consequences and possible solutions.

Part I deals with the types of pollution incident we encounter, methods of damage assessment to human health and the environment, and the economics, politics and practicality of pollution control and hazard assessment. Part II focuses on the problem of nitrates in Jersey's drinking water and the Chernobyl nuclear accident as case studies of pollution. Part III gives students the opportunity of conducting their own research into pollution, using both primary and secondary data sources.

Ian Foster

CONTENTS

Lethal pollutant found in bodies of porpoises

Government refuses ban on 'cancer-link' fruit spra[y]

Inspector to visit Chernobyl site

British output of pollutant gas still increasing

EC clampdown on toxic waste

Tony Heath

A POLLUTANT that causes reproduction failures in marine mamm... has been f...

Nitrates worst in East Anglia water

Salmon farmers likely to avoid pesticide charge

Rob Edwards

ONE of Britain's biggest fish farmers is likely to escape prosecution ov... an incident earlier ... when sever... highly

his decision, although he is not optimistic. Mr Buchanan is also concerned at ... suggestio... the ...

istry of Ag... and F...

Part I
THE POLLUTION PROBLEM

Pollution, Pollution, they got smog and sewage and mud,
Turn on your tap and get hot and cold running crud.

(With apologies to Tom Lehrer)

1 INTRODUCTION

Over the last 20 years there has been a growth in the awareness of environmental pollution problems and pollution has become a major national and international political issue. Indeed, in the 1989 European elections, the Green Party in the UK polled an unprecedented 15 per cent of the votes indicating the strength of feeling among voters on environmental issues. Disasters, such as the oil spillage from the Torrey Canyon tanker off the Scilly Isles (1967), the Exxon Valdez spillage in Alaska (1989), and the Chernobyl nuclear accident in the Soviet Union (1986), have produced devastating effects upon the natural environment as well as creating real dangers to human life (see page 4). Government response to individual incidents has often led to improvements in safety and a reduction in pollution risk: for example, the well-known London smogs of the 1950s were effectively tackled by the *Clean Air Acts*. Yet, once tackled, new problems have arisen to take their place.

Today, there is widespread concern about a broad range of issues. The *acid rain* problem has become more serious, as has the *greenhouse effect* and reduction in thickness of the *ozone layer*. All of these issues are related to different forms of atmospheric pollution. Both fresh and sea waters are polluted by fertilisers, pesticides and insecticides from farmland. They are also affected by discharges from industrial processing plants, by leakage of toxic materials from inland waste disposal sites and by contamination from domestic sewage, even after processing at sewage works. Creation of waste, from nuclear power stations and other industrial processes, leaves us with problems of where to store it and how to treat it.

It is in the light of these wide ranging issues that this book examines some of the major problems facing us in terms of pollution and how to deal with the pollution problem. We will look at some of the health and environmental consequences of pollution and examine some of the conventional and less conventional means of controlling the problem in a range of situations. Before embarking on a lengthy description of a range of pollution problems, however, it is most important to consider *what is pollution?* and *how are people and the environment affected by pollutants?* These questions are important in deciding how and to what extent pollution is likely to become a serious risk.

◀ *Newspaper headlines about pollution issues. The photos show air pollution from a chemical plant on Humberside and attempts to contain and treat an oil spillage in the Gulf of Mexico*

2 THE NATURE AND EXTENT OF ENVIRONMENTAL POLLUTION

2.1 Definitions

A good working definition of pollution is provided by the *Royal Commission on Environmental Pollution* which reported to the government in 1984. In this report, pollution is defined as:

'The introduction by man into the environment of substances or energy liable to cause hazards to human health, harm to living resources and ecological systems, damage to structures or amenity, or interference with legitimate use of the environment.'

(Royal Commission on Environmental Pollution, 1984, p.3)

This definition stresses the influence of human activity on the environment and separates it from natural changes which may occur anyway. However, this makes interpretation of some changes more difficult to identify. For example, recent speculations on the impact of atmospheric pollution on global temperatures and sea level change must be looked at in relation to sea level changes known to have occurred during recent glacial and interglacial times when human activity and interference could not have been responsible (Dawson, 1991).

It is also implied in the above definition of pollution that it is not just the *presence* of a substance which will concern us, but the fact that it has a *harmful effect*, either on human health or on the environment. This often means that at *low concentrations* a substance may be of little or no danger whereas at *high concentrations* it may act as a pollutant. This is why, as we will see later, much of the legislation and guidelines dealing with pollutants will set limits on the concentration rather than *presence or absence* of substances in the environment. In order to identify a substance which has a harmful effect, we will use the term *pollutant*. For a substance which either has no known harmful effects, or is present in very low concentrations and will therefore have a minimal effect upon the environment, we will use the term *contaminant*.

2.2 Assessing damage to health and the environment

It is important when assessing the impact of pollution or estimating pollution damage to obtain information on both the *toxicity* and the *environmental impact* of a particular substance. There are three main objectives in assessing pollution:

1. To determine *thresholds* at which harm or damage occurs.
2. To determine the relationship between the amount (*dose*) of the pollutant ingested or released and the outcome (*response*) of this action.
3. To *measure* the total damage suffered by populations and communities from a pollution incident.

The distinction between a contaminant and a pollutant in relation to the three objectives listed above is difficult to establish and often becomes clearer not through carefully controlled trials or experiments, but by analysis of either accidents in the factory and in the environment or by examining the consequences of the long term release of substances.

For example, at low concentrations, aluminium sulphate is used in water treatment works and is present in *low concentrations* in most water supplies. However, the accidental addition of 20 tons of aluminium sulphate to the drinking water supplies of Camelford, Cornwall on 20th July 1988 caused a number of severe gastric problems, itching rashes and mouth ulcers. The highly acidic water (measured at a pH of between 3.5 and 4.2 instead of the usual 8.0), once recognised as a problem by the South West Water Authority, was flushed from the mains water supplies into the River Camel where it immediately killed most of the fish.

In many situations, however, toxicity data are not available. In the United States, for example, it is estimated that over 70 000 chemical substances are manufactured. For most of these substances there is little information on toxicity, environmental behaviour or likely future impacts on the environment following disposal. For some substances there is much more information, particularly in relation to health effects.

i) Health effects

A number of health effects have been identified in relation to the presence of nitrates in drinking water supplies. Nitrate itself is not toxic, but is converted to nitrite in the human body. Because it is a powerful oxidising agent, it can affect the uptake and distribution of oxygen in the bloodstream, particularly in young babies, causing a condition known as *methaemoglobinaemia* or *blue baby* syndrome. Since first identified in the United States in the 1940s, over 2000 cases have been reported worldwide. (The disease is extremely rare in the UK, with only some 10 recorded cases in the last 30 years and only one of them fatal.) Although a large number of cases have been reported, it is still extremely difficult to determine either the dose or *exposure* (length of time a dose is received) in order to set precise limits on drinking water standards (see section 3.2). The data in each reported case are often not available, and it is difficult to take account of other factors which may make an infant more susceptible to the presence of nitrate.

Other problems arise in relation to the way in which a particular pollutant is taken into the body, and what form the pollutant is in (i.e. liquid, solid or gas). For example, the toxicity of lead has been known for a long time. At low concentrations in the body it is known to cause lethargy whereas at higher concentrations, kidney failure and irreversible brain damage may occur. Earlier this century, the main sources of poisoning were from lead-based paints, often swallowed by children, and from lead water-pipes in the home. This situation has changed since the increase in the number of cars using leaded fuels. Car exhausts now provide a more significant source of lead than lead pipes and lead-based paints (now banned in childrens toys) especially as it readily enters the body through breathing rather than through the stomach (a less efficient way of accumulating lead in body tissue). Although much of the lead falls to the ground close to the source of the pollutant (roads), some is carried further and inhabitants of urban environments are most likely to suffer from increasing lead content through uptake in the lungs. Because of this, lead levels in blood are likely to be higher in the inner city than in the suburbs (Figure 1.1). However, identifying the exact point at which lead becomes dangerously toxic is complex, especially as mild symptoms at low doses such as fatigue, depression and mental retardation may go unnoticed. It is also difficult to find the levels at which a pollutant becomes toxic because the effects may be *cumulative* due to exposure for long periods of time.

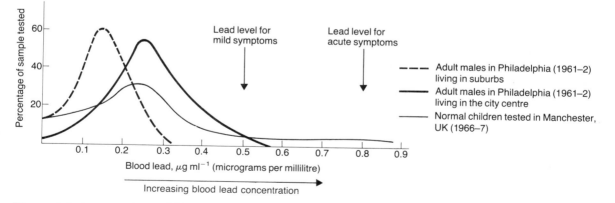

Figure 1.1 *A comparison of blood lead concentrations in adults and children in Philadelphia (USA) and Manchester (UK) to show the effects of living in the centre of major cities. The levels at which mild and severe lead poisoning symptoms occur are also indicated*

Some substances are not toxic if ingested rather than inhaled. For example, mercury is not very poisonous if taken by mouth; an adult may tolerate up to 30 g per day. However, mercury vapour is very toxic when inhaled in small quantities.

ii) Environmental effects

Identification of harmful effects on the environment, rather than human health, may be easier to establish either through laboratory experiments or through long term monitoring. However, the impacts are often complex and require many years of experimentation and observation before a complete picture is revealed.

For example, since the early 1970s, debate has focused on the increasing acidity of rainfall which has been caused, in part, by the release of sulphur and nitrogen compounds into the atmosphere by burning fossil fuels in power stations and petrol engines. These gases may dissolve in rain droplets which will comprise solutions of nitric and sulphuric acids. It has been found that some areas of the country have river waters and soils which are more susceptible to the effects of this *acid rain* than others (Figure 1.2). If we compare this map with a geological map it will be apparent that the areas of high and medium susceptibility correlate with areas which are not capable of *buffering* the acid inputs. Buffering of acids occurs by neutralising the acid with an alkali. In chemical weathering, the process is called *acid hydrolysis*. Here, the hydrogen from the acid forms a new non-acidic substance. Rocks and soils containing large amounts of neutralising substances, especially calcium and magnesium carbonates, will have a high *buffering capacity* and can neutralise acid inputs more easily than other rocks and soils. This means that both soils and fresh waters are less likely to become acidic in areas of low susceptibility. For example, in Figure 1.2, large areas of Dartmoor, North Wales and the Lake District have little capacity to neutralise acid inputs whereas areas of Hampshire, Midland England and the Central Lowlands of Scotland have soils and rocks with a high buffering capacity.

Many impacts of acid rain have been identified. For example, a severe decline in the fish populations of North West Europe and Canada have been linked to an increase in rainfall acidity. The relationship between this effect and its believed

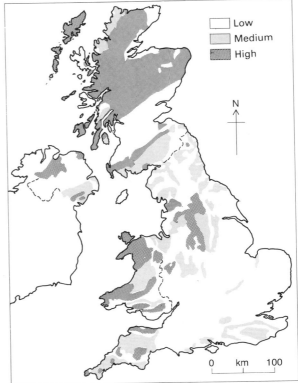

Figure 1.2 *Areas of the United Kingdom which have high, medium and low susceptibility to the input of acid rain*

cause is not simple and direct. Laboratory experiments have shown that rainbow trout exposed to acid water for 3 days begin to show changes in blood chemistry and circulation. However, the *lethal effects* of acid rain are associated not only with acidity, but the effect that it has on the solubility of toxic heavy metals, especially aluminium (see the Camelford pollution incident, page 6). For example, Figure 1.3 shows the relationship between the concentration of aluminium in relation to pH in Swedish lakes. pH is a measure of acidity defined as the concentration of hydrogen ions in water. The scale ranges from 1 (very acid) to 14 (alkali) with a value of 7 being neutral. The scale is *logarithmic* (the logarithm to the base 10 of the concentration). At pH 7, there are 10^{-7} (0.0000001) *moles* (a measure of

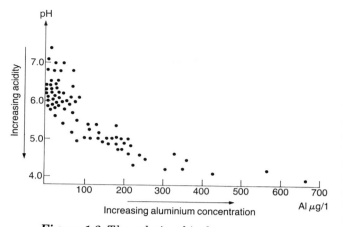

Figure 1.3 *The relationship between pH and total aluminium concentration in some Swedish lakes*

nitrogen (N) and phosphorus (P) to farmland increases productivity. However, over-use has resulted in a common problem in Europe and North America known as *eutrophication*. With a change to eutrophic conditions, freshwater bodies show dramatic changes from clear deepwater habitats, with good oxygenation of the waters, high species diversity and with trout and other white fish present (an unpolluted or *oligotrophic condition*) to water of poor visibility, low oxygen levels, rapid sedimentation and the presence of only coarse fish like roach and bream (a highly polluted or *hypertrophic condition*). Many changes occur in rivers and lakes as a result of increasing their nutrient content and some of these are summarised in Table 1.1.

2.3 Identifying the source

i) Point and diffuse sources

Pollutants enter the environment from a number of sources which can broadly be divided into two groups: *point* and *non-point* sources. Point sources are those where a *point of emission* can be identified on the ground, such as a sewage outfall pipe, an industrial effluent or a power station chimney discharging into the atmosphere. Non-point sources include pollutants which enter the environment from a *diffuse* rather than a point source. Particularly important here is the application of agrochemicals, such as herbicides, insecticides and fertilisers, to soils and water courses. Other diffuse sources include domestic refuse and industrial wastes which often require reprocessing to make them less harmful or reduce

concentration) of hydrogen dissolved in the water. At pH 5, there are 10^{-5}(0.00001 moles of hydrogen per litre of water); 100 times as much. Each one unit reduction in pH, therefore, means *an order of magnitude increase in acidity*. Under normal environmental conditions, aluminium remains in soil minerals and is not released into the environment. However, at low pH, aluminium and other metals are released and its presence will affect many parts of the life cycle of fish species, from the development of eggs through survival of young fish.

Many substances in the environment occur naturally and may be essential for the healthy growth and development of ecological systems. It is well known, for example, that the addition of

Table 1.1 Changes in some properties of fresh waters associated with eutrophication

Pollution level	Trophic status	Visibility[c] (m)	Primary productivity (g cm^{-2} yr^{-1})	Algae[a] (g m^{-3})	Total P[b] (mg m^3)	Total N[b] (mg m^3)	Fish type
Low	Oligotrophic	over 5	less than 30	less than 0.8	less than 5	less than 300	Trout White Fish
Medium	Mesotrophic	3–6	25–60	0.3–1.9	5–20	300–500	White Fish Perch
	Eutrophic	1–4	40–200	1.2–2.5	20–100	350–600	Perch Roach
High	Hypertrophic	0–2	130–600	2.1–20	over 100	over 1000	Roach Bream

a = mean for period May–October. b = mean for Spring. c = using Secci disk (see Part III).

the volume to be tipped. This process demands an infrastructure for collection, treatment and disposal. Many of the environmental pollutants which originate from a diffuse source are treated at discrete points in the environment, such as in incinerators, land-fill sites or in specialised reprocessing centres such as the Windscale reprocessing plant dealing with spent nuclear fuels at Sellafield, Cumbria.

ii) The importance of time

It is possible to subdivide the above twofold classification by introducing a time dimension. For example, some point sources are fixed in space and repeatedly release pollution into the environment. Others are randomly located in space and through time, like accidents. This latter subdivision includes *accidental spillages* of hazardous materials during transport, through such events as road and rail accidents and shipwrecks, and other events such as fires breaking out in chemical factories or power stations.

iii) Effects of transportation

Although point sources may be identified, the pollutants themselves, once released, may travel great distances and enter some parts of the environment as a diffuse rather than a point source. This is particularly apparent with a change in the *phase* of pollutant transport. For example, the acid rain problem derives from liberation of waste gases (*the gas phase*) from point sources, like factory chimneys. However, atmospheric reactions and the solution of these gases in falling precipitation creates acid rain (*the liquid phase*). Acid rain will often be diffuse and widespread. Many industrial atmospheric emissions also include fine dusts (*the solid phase*) which may be deposited in a dry state but may subsequently dissolve during rainstorms. Even that polluted dust which does not dissolve may be transported physically by falling and flowing water both over the land surface and in rivers.

iv) Effects of chemical reactions

A further complicating factor in understanding pollution problems is the type of reaction between the pollutant and the environment in which it is transported. For example, many agrochemicals, such as the important plant nutrient nitrogen (in

the form of nitrate) is highly soluble and may be carried away from fields in solution towards rivers and lakes. Other nutrients, such as phosphorus, are only slightly soluble under normal conditions and are transported with the soil as it is eroded from fields and reaches streams with suspended sediment. A similar problem is associated with the transport of herbicides, pesticides and fungicides which may be transported in solution, with suspended sediment or as a combination of the two.

2.4 Examples of different pollutant sources

This section will look at examples and case studies of the different sources of pollution identified above. It is important to be aware of the wide range of pollutants and their effects since pollution control measures and legislation must be designed to tackle all pollution forms.

i) Fixed point sources

a) Acid rain

Many of the environmental problems causing national and international concern at the present time derive from point source pollution. In particular, the acid rain problem has been related to emissions of nitrogen, sulphur and chlorine gases from three major sources; power stations, car exhausts and the combustion of fossil fuels in domestic fires. Once in the atmosphere, these gases undergo a series of chemical transformations to produce strong acids, particularly nitric (HNO_3), sulphuric (H_2SO_4) and hydrochloric acid (HCl). These strong acids are added to naturally occurring weak acids, especially carbonic acid (H_2CO_3), which gives *natural rain* a slightly acid pH of around 5.6. However, these strong acids will lower pH levels considerably and, on one occasion in the UK, a pH of 2.0 has been recorded in rainfall. The results of these acid releases into the environment are widespread. Figure 1.4 shows the pH of rainfall for the United Kingdom. The effects of acid rain are not necessarily direct, but often operate in combination with other chemicals in the environment, such as ozone, and through the release of toxic substances such as aluminium into soils, rivers and lakes (see page 8). The consequences so far identified include:

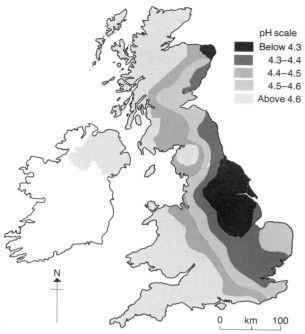

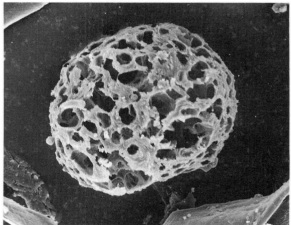

Figure 1.5 Indicators of atmospheric pollution in lake sediment studies

a A diatom skeleton (Cyclotella meneghiniana)

Figure 1.4 Acidity of UK rainfall, 1987

pH scale
Below 4.3
4.3–4.4
4.4–4.5
4.5–4.6
Above 4.6

b A magnified carbonaceous particle, the result of industrial air pollution

1. Destruction of forests, thought to be caused by the liberation of heavy metals like aluminium into soils by strong acids.
2. Deterioration in fish stocks, thought to relate to the effects of both acids themselves and the heavy metals released into lakes and rivers.
3. Increased weathering of building stones and increasing rates of chemical weathering processes in the natural environment, caused by reactions to the acid content of the rainfall.

One of the great problems in the acid rain debate has been to show that increasing acidification of surface waters and soils is a recent phenomenon and directly related to the increase in fossil fuel consumption in recent years. It is important to demonstrate that this process is not associated with other environmental changes. For example, soils and waters in some areas might have become more acid as a result of the replacement of traditional broad-leaved forests with more acidifying coniferous plantations, particularly of spruce. However, the problem is so widespread that local issues are unlikely to have

more than spatially limited effects. These issues have been tackled through a range of scientific investigations, but of great importance has been the study of sediments which accumulate in the bottom of lakes and reservoirs. Within this sediment are the remains of a group of organisms called *diatoms* which once inhabited the lake waters (Figure 1.5a). Their silicon skeletons are preserved in the sediment as it is deposited over time. In addition to these organisms, there are soot particles which are easily identifiable under high powered magnification (Figure 1.5b). These particles come from power stations and other fossil fuel burning industrial plants. Some species of diatom are particularly sensitive to changes in the pH of lake waters and therefore different species will have been deposited in the sediments at different periods of time if the pH has changed.

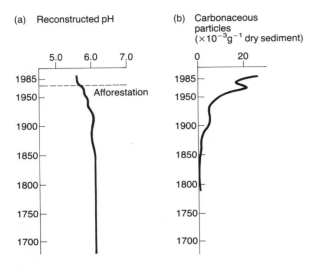

Figure 1.6 *The 'reconstructed' pH (a) (based on diatom analysis) and the carbonaceous particle content (b) of a lake sediment core from Llyn Cwm Mynach, Central Wales*

Lake sediments are therefore rather like a time capsule with age increasing as we dig deeper into the sediment. By looking at the change in species remains at different depths in the sediment, it is possible to *reconstruct* what the pH of a lake has been over long periods of time (Figure 1.6). For example, in Llyn Cwm Mynach, near Dolgellau, Wales, it appears that variations in acidity are strongly associated with atmospheric pollution since the fall in pH starts at the same time at which soot particles are found. The introduction of upland forestry in this area took place *after* the lake waters started to become more acid but may have added to the acidity problem.

b) Heavy metals

Atmospheric pollution from sources identified above and from other manufacturing and waste incineration processes liberate not only gases but a range of other substances, such as heavy metals (e.g. lead, copper, nickel, cadmium and zinc), some of which are known to be toxic. These heavy metals can be transported long distances in the atmosphere as dusts and are often found in remote locations. For example, Figure 1.7 shows the concentration of lead in lake sediments taken from a range of UK regions, in comparison with estimates of global emissions of lead into the atmosphere for the last 150 years. Sediments are

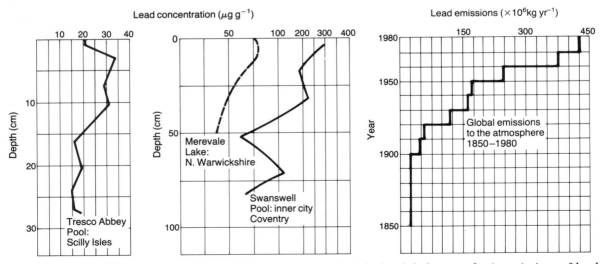

Figure 1.7 *Lead concentrations in lake sediments compared with the global atmospheric emissions of lead for the period 1850–1980*

collected with specially designed equipment which provides an undisturbed sample, up to 1 m long, at the bed of the lake (a sediment core) and may cover deposition which has taken place over several decades or even hundreds of years. In samples from the Scilly Isles where there are few local sources of heavy metals, there is still an increase in concentration towards the sediment surface. Here the recent increases in lead concentration may come from long range transport of heavy metals across the Atlantic Ocean since there is a predominantly south westerly wind in the region. The sites in Midland England have much higher metals concentrations in their surface sediments and, over the last 150 years, the inner city site of Coventry has received about ten times as much heavy metals pollution as the rural site from atmospheric sources alone. This happens because in urban areas there are many local sources of atmospheric pollution, especially motor vehicle exhaust fumes.

In the UK, there are many other forms of point source pollution. Table 1.2 provides some statistics on the number of pollution incidents from different sources in UK rivers and Figure 1.8 provides a review of the chemical quality of rivers provided from a recent national survey. (The data of Table 1.2 will be used in exercises in Part III.)

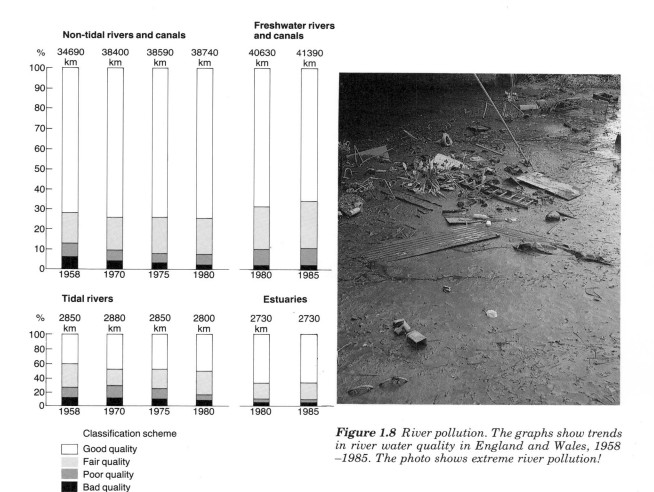

Figure 1.8 *River pollution. The graphs show trends in river water quality in England and Wales, 1958–1985. The photo shows extreme river pollution!*

Table 1.2 Water pollution in England and Wales

a) Water pollution incidents in England and Wales, 1980–87

Water Authority	1980	1981	1982	1983	1984	1985	1986	1987
Anglian	968	1095	1077	1288	1544	1707	1468	1605
Northumbrian	501	509	544	613	654	722	729	671
North West	1290	1350	1288	1385	2241	2202	2480	2961
Severn-Trent	2583	2401	2681	3354	4372	4524	4497	4435
Southern	1196	1300	1327	1400	1574	1668	1725	1795
South West	1060	1143	1227	1639	1685	1796	2220	2251
Thames	1930	1810	2120	2345	2486	2695	2890	2969
Welsh	—	—	—	—	1418	1681	1619	2489
Wessex	871	844	790	966	1125	993	1332	1339
Yorkshire	1071	1136	1020	1165	1536	2006	2444	2738
England and Wales	12500	12600	13100	15400	18635	19994	21404	23253

b) Water pollution incidents in England and Wales classified by cause, 1987

Water Authority	Industrial			Farm	Sewage		Sewerage	Other	All causes	Nothing found
	Oil	Chemical	Other		Own	Other				
Anglian	603	114	66	223	←	381	→	218	1605	
Northumbrian	128	←	42 →		94	←	232	→	122	618	53
North West	494	←	336 →	539	63	91	306	427	2256	705
Severn-Trent	1078	402	383	654	143	30	707	1038	4435	
Southern	483	←	181 →	189	116	125	79	496	1669	126
South West	208	←	252 →	666	←	427	→	371	1924	327
Thames	861	←	190 →	182	←	423	→	568	2489	745
Welsh	←	370	→	716	←	402	→	1001	2489	
Wessex	393	←	52 →	271	←	129	→	251	1096	243
Yorkshire	402	322	215	336	← 261 →		262	525	2323	415
England and Wales	←	7575	→	3870	←	4177	→	5017	20639	2614

c) Performance of sewage treatment plants in England and Wales in relation to consents, 1986–87

	% equivalent of population served by sewage treatment plant failing consents		% equivalent of population served by sewage treatment plant failing consents
Anglian	43	South West	57
Northumbrian	13	Thames	13
North West	26	Welsh	34
Severn-Trent	32	Wessex	36
Southern	24	Yorkshire	46

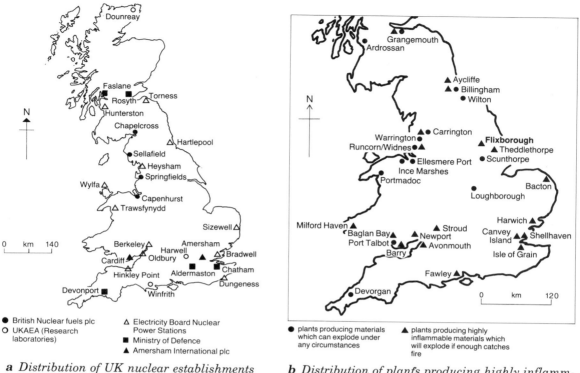

a *Distribution of UK nuclear establishments*

b *Distribution of plants producing highly inflamm-able and explosive materials*

Figure 1.9 *Possible locations of major environmental accidents*

ii) Random point sources

It would be possible to catalogue a whole host of pollution incidents under this heading, since accidental spillage of oil waste at sea, accidents in chemical and nuclear plants and inadvertent release of chemicals into water courses generally prompt national and often international media coverage. Such incidents have important implications for human health as well as for the natural environment and occur despite legislative and engineering improvements designed to minimise the risk involved. These events are included under a random point source here because the location of such problems are unpredictable in both space and time, and the centres from which accidents could occur are widespread (Figure 1.9).

One of the more recent and dramatic incidents involved the fire at the Chernobyl nuclear power station in 1986. This forms the focus of a detailed case study in Part II, but is not the first recorded incident of its type. For example, in October 1957 the first major atmospheric release of nuclear waste from a commercial rather than military installation followed a major fire at Windscale in Cumbria. Radioactive material moved across England, into France, across Northern Europe and into Scandinavia (Figure 1.10). Later calculations undertaken by the National Radiological Protection Board (NRPB) have suggested that an increase in thyroid cancers were likely to result from this accident but at statistically undetectable levels. A similar radioactive cloud release occurred at Three Mile Island, near Harrisburg, Pennsylvania, on 31st March 1979. There were no immediate fatalities, but in the following year, a survey of health records in the neighbourhood revealed much higher numbers of miscarriages and babies born with deformed thyroid glands than before the accident.

Accidents have also occurred in non-nuclear

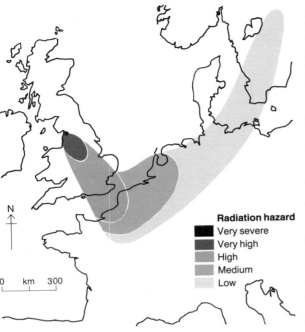

Table 1.3 Estimates of the amount of oil entering the environment in a typical year

Sources	Tonnes
1 Marine operational losses:	
tankers	1 000 000
bilge discharges	300 000
2 Marine accidents,	
all sources	350 000
3 Offshore production	150 000
Natural seepage	600 000
4 Land-based discharges:	
refineries, wastes etc.	1 300 000

Figure 1.10 *The path of radioactive deposition following the Windscale fire of October 1957*

installations. One of the worst recorded incidents occurred in a chemical factory in Seveso, Italy, in July 1976. Here, the accidental release of dioxin into the environment seriously affected trees and vegetation and a large number of animals died soon afterwards. By June 1977, there were 135 reported incidents of a skin disease (*chloracne*) and a new outbreak of the same disease followed in December 1977. Similar events occurred after an accident in a dioxin plant at Bhopal, India, in 1987.

Many accidental spillages of pollutants in the natural environment occur during transport, and through poor management of the transport facility. Of widespread concern are oil spillages during transport, although oil may enter coastal waters from many other sources (Table 1.3). Many major accidents have been reported in recent years. For example, on Good Friday 1989 the oil tanker Exxon Valdez hit an iceberg in Prince William Sound, Alaska (Figure 1.12), discharging 11 million gallons of crude oil which rapidly spread over an area of 1000 square miles. Response to the accident did not occur until 36 hours after the spillage, and the subsequent *clean-up*

operation was fraught with legal, technical and political difficulties. The environmental consequences of this accident are still unclear. Economically, the spillage has had a profound effect on fishing in Alaskan coastal ports where around 2000 people depend upon the fishing industry for their livelihood. In environmental terms, at least 10 000 seabirds died, including species like the bald eagle which is already on the endangered species list, and the consequences for migrating sea birds, salmon and marine mammals are still

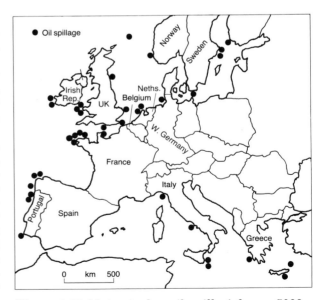

Figure 1.11 *Major tanker oil spills (of over 5000 barrels) known to have occurred in West European waters since 1970*

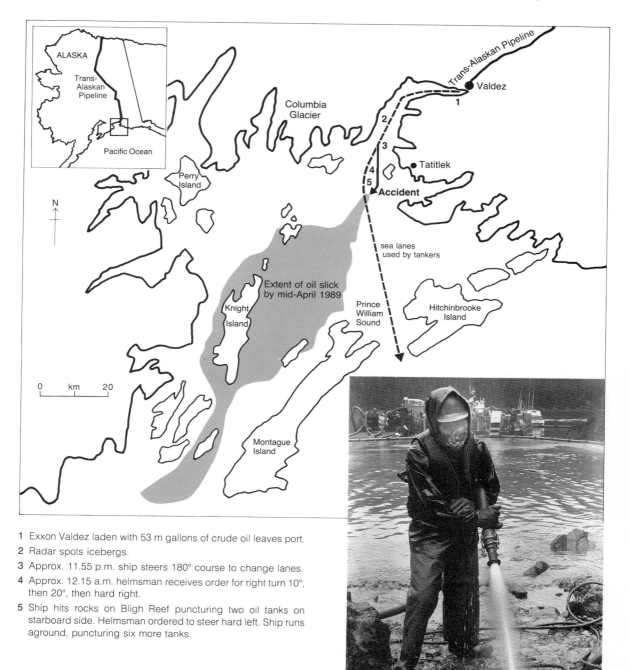

1 Exxon Valdez laden with 53 m gallons of crude oil leaves port.
2 Radar spots icebergs.
3 Approx. 11.55 p.m. ship steers 180° course to change lanes.
4 Approx. 12.15 a.m. helmsman receives order for right turn 10°, then 20°, then hard right.
5 Ship hits rocks on Bligh Reef puncturing two oil tanks on starboard side. Helmsman ordered to steer hard left. Ship runs aground, puncturing six more tanks.

Figure 1.12 *The Exxon Valdez oil spillage in Alaska. The photo shows part of the clean-up operation*

unknown. Estimates of the cost of the clean-up operation range from £60 billion to £120 billion. By early April 1989 only some half a million gallons had been recovered and, because of rapid dispersal, there was little chance that more than the same amount would be collected in the immediate aftermath. In Europe, major oil spillages from tankers have occurred in the last ten years at a rate approaching two a year (Figure 1.11).

Additional hazards are posed by oil exploration in the North Sea. For example, in the Ekofisk oil field, located in the Norwegian sector of the North Sea, the Bravo drilling rig experienced a blow-out in April 1977 releasing 20 000 tons of crude oil. Such dangers were further underlined by the Piper Alpha oil rig fire in July 1988 when 150 workers were killed on site.

iii) Non-point sources

Non-point sources provide somewhat different problems for control and management than point sources. This problem will be examined briefly here through a consideration of UK agricultural practices.

Several pollutants have come from land management practices, particularly in the last 150 years, when there has been a major increase in the consumption of fertilisers, herbicides, insecti-

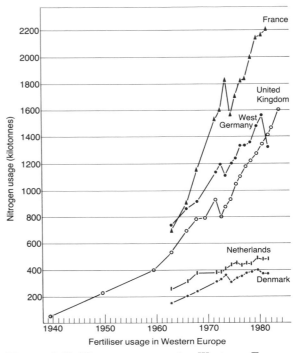

Figure 1.13 *Nitrogen usage in Western Europe, 1940–84*

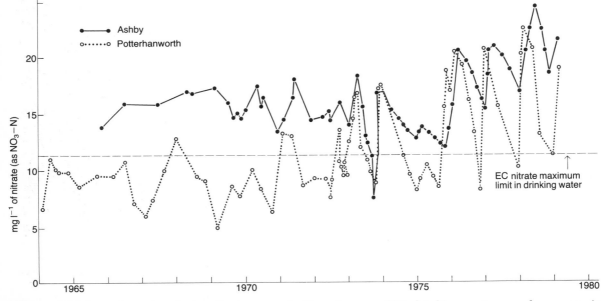

Figure 1.14 *Long term trends in nitrate concentrations in some UK drinking water supply sources in Lincolnshire*

cides and pesticides (Figure 1.13). A number of chemicals which occur naturally in the environment are added to soils as fertilisers, to change soil acidity levels or to destroy harmful pests; these include nitrogen, phosphorus, potassium, calcium and, to a lesser extent, sodium, chlorine, magnesium and sulphur. The addition of nitrogen and phosphorus to soils, for example, is known to cause eutrophication in rivers and lakes (see page 9) but the exact effect that these and other chemicals have on soil and water depends on a number of factors. One of the most important is the *solubility* of the chemical (the rate and amount of a chemical which will dissolve). Nitrogen, in the form of nitrate, is highly soluble and trends in nitrate concentrations in British drinking water sources (Figure 1.14) can be compared with the trends in fertiliser import and usage given in Figure 1.13. Increases in concentration are certainly not uniform throughout the country (Figure 1.15), and certain areas seem to be more susceptible than others. This is partly because of the spatial variations in fertiliser application rates and partly because of the different types of soil found in the UK. Sandy soils which drain quickly may lose nitrogen more rapidly than clay soils for example.

Long term changes in river water nitrate levels are affected by many agricultural management factors. These include industrialisation and increased mechanisation of agriculture, the increasing application of agrochemicals and the influence of the European Community's Common Agricultural Policy on farming in the UK (Ilbery, 1991).

Particularly severe pollution incidents may follow extreme meteorological conditions and in turn may lead to restrictions on water use at times of shortage. A good example of this problem arose in the UK during and immediately after our most extreme drought in recent years in 1976. Widespread crop failure resulted in the accumulation of unused fertilisers in soils. These accumulations were rapidly flushed into rivers during heavy rain in September and October 1976 which caused a widespread increase in stream nitrate concentrations. Similarly, the long hot summer of 1989 gave rise to pollution incidents, particularly in East Anglian reservoirs, where the abundant growth of microscopic plants (*algae*) led to the closure of reservoirs for

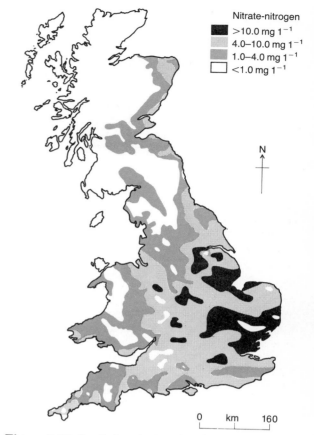

Figure 1.15 *Spatial variations in nitrate concentrations in UK river waters*

recreation. These growths occurred because of increasing amounts of phosphorus reaching the reservoirs.

Changes in the use of pesticides, insecticides and herbicides are difficult to measure because, until 1986, provision for making returns on their use was not statutory. Since the *Food and Environment Protection Act* of 1985, details of applications and types of pesticide in use must be registered with the Ministry of Agriculture Fisheries and Food (MAFF). Surveys indicate that by the year 1978, over 800 chemicals appeared on the approved chemicals list. Up to 1939, the chemical control of pests was undertaken using a limited range of products often produced by synthesising natural organic products such as nicotine, which had been used in Europe since about 1700 AD. The modern agroche-

Figure 1.16 *Aerial insecticide application on a potato crop. Spraying is not limited to the crop!*

mical industry, developed since the Second World War, produced over 50 new herbicides, pesticides and insecticides at its peak in 1968. One of the more important developments occurred with the introduction of aerial spraying of crops (Figure 1.16). In 1987, over 200 000 ha of agricultural land were treated with pesticides in this way.

2.5 Assessing the risk

Environmental pollution clearly poses risks of potential disaster either to health or the environment, some of which are much easier to estimate than others. For example, it may be easier to calculate the impact of a new industrial processing plant on atmospheric and water pollution than the effects of powerful agricultural chemicals on water courses, often because such chemicals are introduced before a full investigation of environmental consequences has taken place. These chemicals may harm people who have not

specifically chosen to accept the consequences of their use and, more frequently, do not know of their widespread application. In this instance, it is important that a regulatory authority of some kind be given powers to act on behalf of individuals to minimise the potential risks.

Of course we often take *calculated risks*, and the decision to accept or reject such risks is often a matter of personal or political judgement rather than calculated fact. In the case of an individual who smokes ten cigarettes a day, he or she has a 1 in 400 chance of dying prematurely. About 1 in 4 regular smokers is killed by smoking! Such certainty of potential hazard has been derived from statistical analysis of the health records of smokers and provides an individual with a good basis on how to make a decision whether or not to smoke. However, the institutional and government response may be very different. Many organisations argue that, because of pressure from industry, taxes are insufficiently high to *protect the consumer*. The tobacco industry has a powerful political lobby and, as a result of a reduction in the number of smokers in the UK and USA and restrictions on advertising, has responded by changing marketing strategy (trying to sell more cigarettes to the developing world) in order to protect the interests of shareholders and employees alike. These two groups are at risk if government action reduces product sales. Similar arguments are, of course, relevant to all industrial processes where environmental pollution results directly from a manufacturing base and the implementation of stronger pollution control measures may result in a loss of competitive edge and increasing unemployment.

In some areas of the UK, attempts have been made to assess the overall hazard from pollution. For example, in a study of Greater Manchester, six measures of pollution in different forms were added together as an aggregate score of pollution potential (see Part III for explanation). The composite map of Greater Manchester (Figure 1.17) is divided into 71 local authority areas. High overall pollution levels are generally found around Salford, in the centre of the conurbation and around Wigan. These high pollution levels often occur in areas of low socio-economic status highlighting a further dimension to problems of inner

city deprivation and re-development (Matthews, 1991).

It is extremely difficult to assess all hazards arising from pollution. The assessment would require estimates of financial losses, for example, resulting from employee absence at the workplace. We might also try to calculate the cost of injury (medical costs) and death (loss of breadwinner from a family) caused by different pollutants. Since these statistics are difficult to obtain, the hazard is often assessed by comparing risk of death from pollution with the risks involved in natural hazards. We might, for example, decide to accept the risk if the probability of premature death is about the same as that associated with a lightning strike. Risks above this level may be considered unacceptable, and attempts would be made to improve pollution control in order to reduce the risk. The problems highlighted above assume that we can:

1 Identify the risk
2 Estimate the risk
3 Evaluate the risk
4 Control the risk

This can be achieved in some cases by learning from past experiences or by transferring experiences from a similar situation. Attempts to evaluate risk in new types of industry often cannot use past experience or direct comparisons with similar situations which do not exist. In 1975, for example, the *Rasmussen Report* of the Atomic Energy Commission attempted to assess the consequences of an extremely serious nuclear accident (a melt-down of the reactor core) in terms of fatalities and illnesses (Table 1.4) and calculated that the chance of a melt-down would be in the region of 1 in 200 million years. Following the Three Mile Island incident, a Ford Foundation study group report concluded that the probability

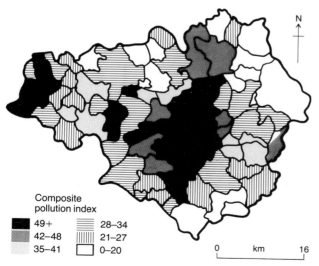

Figure 1.17 *A pollution index for the Greater Manchester area*

Composite pollution index

49+   28–34
42–48 21–27
35–41 0–20

0   km   16

Table 1.4 Estimates of the possible consequences of an extremely serious accident in the nuclear power industry

Prompt fatalities	3300
Early illness	45000
Thyroid nodules	240000 over 30 years
Latent cancer fatalities	45000 over 30 years
Genetic defects	30000 over 150 years

Economic loss due to contamination $14 billion
Decontamination area 8300 km^2

of a melt-down in a nuclear power station before the year 2000 AD was reduced to 1 in 4! The error in risk assessment did not allow, as we will see later in the Chernobyl incident, for a catalogue of wrong decisions taken by individuals in the plant, the probabilities of which were never estimated or even considered possible.

Of course, we are at risk in the environment from natural as well as artificially produced radiation (Figure 1.18). Eighty-seven per cent of the radiation received in the UK in 1987 was from natural sources, of which radon (a radioactive gas emitted from granitic rocks in particular) makes up well over half. The risk associated with radon is not uniformly distributed, since highest levels are to be found in South West England and in parts of Central Wales. Of the 13 per cent of artificial radiation received, over 92 per cent comes from medical sources and the remainder from industrial processes and atmospheric fallout.

We can see from the above arguments that there is a considerable degree of uncertainty in

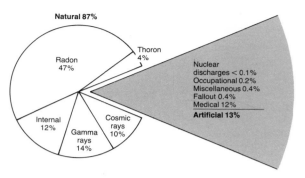

Figure 1.18 *Sources of radiation dosages received by the UK population for the year 1987*

assessing risk or hazard from pollution events. We see this regularly in our newspapers (page 4) under headings like 'Inadequacies in Tanker Design Leads to Major Pollution Incident' which emphasises the point that events leading to accidents constantly surprise us and are, therefore, impossible to predict.

3   POLLUTION CONTROL

Many different pollution control strategies are available which may limit the environmental and human impacts described in earlier sections. In this section, we will examine a range of alternative pollution control strategies before looking at the involvement of the European Community, economic considerations and international problems of pollution control.

3.1 Alternative strategies

There are nine major strategies which can be used to reduce the risk of pollution incidents. These will be examined under their relevant headings with examples.

i) Prevent accident or spillage

Accident prevention may be achieved by improvements in technology and by regulating or controlling certain activities. For example, improvements in ship design will reduce the chance of accidental spillage, and the introduction of a set of strict guidelines for the transport of toxic or

potentially toxic wastes will minimise the risk. All road container lorries must be clearly marked when transporting hazardous chemicals and radioactive materials. Accident prevention may also involve the selection of less harmful but equally effective substances: the chemical DDT has now been banned for pest control in Europe.

ii) Remove pollution from sensitive areas

Removing chemicals to *safe areas* may minimise immediate risk, but may create new problems at the point of disposal. For example Bazalgette's famous London sewerage scheme was developed between 1850 and 1865. It was designed to divert sewage from the city centre to an outflow some 18 km downstream of London Bridge, thereby transferring the problem from the point of greatest environmental risk (especially to health) into what was seen at the time as a safe discharge point for untreated effluent.

In the last five years, interest has focused upon limiting the possibility of pollutants reaching surface waters and shallow groundwater systems where they move freely to other parts of the environment, especially to rivers, lakes and oceans. For example, the deep-well disposal of liquid wastes from trade and industry appears to be a method which, according to a 1985 report for UNESCO and the World Meteorological Organisation (WMO):

'will increasingly be employed in numerous countries where it is geologically possible and environmentally sound.'

The process requires the construction of deep boreholes into so called *receiving units* which will not allow the pollutants to circulate outside of the confined area (Figure 1.19). Similar proposals have been made for the disposal of low and intermediate level radioactive wastes.

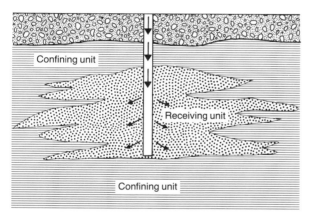

Figure 1.19 *Methods used for the deep disposal of hazardous wastes; here using a 'safe' geological stratum*

iii) Reduce the vulnerability of the pollution target

This is not a widespread strategy for pollution control, although some pollution problems have been controlled in this way. For example, it is possible to ensure that infants are fed on bottled water in water supply areas with high nitrate levels in order to minimise the possible risk of *blue baby* syndrome (see page 7).

iv) Treat harmful substances before release

This is a widespread strategy and could involve the treatment of wastes on site during the manu-

facturing process. This is illustrated by the treatment of flue gases from incinerators and power station chimneys in order to reduce the output of toxic material into the atmosphere.

An alternative strategy is to treat waste in specialised reprocessing plants, a method now commonly employed to treat PCBs (*polychlorinated biphenyls*). PCBs are a group of chemical compounds which were first used in the United States in 1929 as insulating, fire resistant fluids. They are present in electrical installations, paints and plastics and have been associated with a number of pollution incidents. In the 1960s, for example, over 1500 Japanese became ill after eating PCB contaminated rice. Toxicological effects of PCBs include damage to human liver and nervous systems. At the present time, they are disposed of through controlled burning at a constant temperature in incinerators such as in the ReChem plant, near Pontypool, South Wales. Recycling of these wastes, and the import of PCBs from Canada for recycling at Pontypool, gave rise in 1989 to widespread public opposition as we will see later (page 26).

v) Develop alternative technologies

Application of alternative technologies will often follow from severe pollution incidents. The London smogs of the early 1950s were tackled by the *Clean Air Act* of 1952 and, following this Act, industry began to change from coal to oil fired power stations and industrial complexes which reduced smoke levels in the UK. Similar developments are taking place following the establishment of the link between acid rain and the output of sulphur dioxide from power stations. Here, the installation of scrubbers in power station chimney stacks will remove a high proportion of sulphur dioxide which once reached the atmosphere. Many politicians have argued that the acid rain problem could be solved by increasing the proportion of electricity generated by nuclear power stations in the UK!

vi) Alter the demand for products

By extending the lifetime of a product, it is possible to minimise the frequency of its replacement and reduce pollution derived from both initial manufacture and from eventual disposal of the product. Improvements in metal treatment, in theory, increases the life expectancy of cars and

Table 1.5 Trends in the recycling of waste in England and Wales, 1982–87

Waste collection: reclamation of glass,
waste paper and abandoned vehicles

	1982/3	*1983/4*	*1984/5*	*1985/6*	*1986/7*
Number of bottle banks	1029	2046	2572	3076	3089
Amount of glass recovered from bottle banks (thousand tonnes)	46	67	63	76	70
Amount of glass recovered from all sources (thousand tonnes)	110	128	162	210	228
% of authorities operating waste paper collection scheme	14	11	12	10	9
Amount of paper recovered (thousand tonnes)	48	41	42	34	29
Number of abandoned vehicles recovered (thousands)	40	38	25	21	16

Source: *Waste Collection Statistics*

should limit the need to increase the production rate. However, unless consumer behaviour is also modified (see ix below) this strategy is unlikely to have a dramatic impact on pollution control.

vii) Recycle materials

Recycling is a response which has increased in the UK over the last decade, especially in relation to domestic refuse, but of course has a long history in ferrous and non-ferrous metal reprocessing. Many Waste Collection Authorities encourage the recycling of glass, tin cans and waste paper (Table 1.5). This has a twofold impact on pollution levels. First, it reduces pollution from waste disposal and secondly from waste produced in the primary manufacturing process.

viii) Site the source of pollution away from sensitive areas

In a heavily populated region like the United Kingdom, this type of response is difficult to achieve. However, most nuclear power stations have been deliberately located in coastal areas or in regions which are, as far as possible, remote from major centres of population (Figure 1.9).

ix) Modify consumer behaviour

We all share a collective responsibility for pollution because we all demand goods and services which cannot be provided without some damage being done to the environment. Modification of consumer behaviour is often an important first

step in the successful implementation of pollution control strategies, especially those listed in i, iii, vi and vii above. It is well demonstrated by the widespread appearance of bottlebanks, can banks and waste paper collectors near supermarkets during the 1980s. However, their success requires consumer cooperation in order to recycle waste economically. Examples are also to be found on supermarket shelves since 1989, when numerous brands of ecologically safe detergents and recycled packaging materials became widely available. Consumers therefore have a choice of environmentally less harmful materials.

From the above options, it becomes clear that a wide range of strategies are available for minimising or reducing the risk from pollution incidents and from the accumulation of toxic substances and contaminants in the environment. In response to this list, we can look at other ways such pollution levels may be minimised by government intervention. A number of strategies are available, from the exercise of positive incentives, such as the setting of lower tax limits on ecologically less harmful products, to the setting of strict guidelines and standards on emissions, discharges and industrial health and safety which have the force of law. We will first examine the setting of *pollution standards*.

3.2 Setting standards

There are a number of ways by which standards are set, depending on the nature of the pollutant involved. These are briefly outlined below with examples.

i) Ambient standards

These are sometimes called environmental quality standards, and refer to the allowed levels of a pollutant in the environment. They have been adopted by law in many countries (e.g. USA, USSR and Japan) in relation to air pollution but not in the UK. In Britain, for example, the Water Companies (Formerly Water Authorities), have tackled pollution by specifying what are called *Quality Objectives*. These have no standing in law, but are simply targets for water quality which can be met in a number of ways, especially by using *Performance Standards*.

ii) Performance standards

These deal with levels of treatment before discharge or emission into the environment. For example, in the UK, the Alkali and Clean Air Inspectorate set standards for atmospheric emissions and the National Rivers Authority issue licences, including quality criteria, for the discharge of industrial and sewage effluent into water courses. A second type of performance standard relating to point source pollution is known as the *Design Standard*, which specifies how the objective set by the performance standard is to be achieved. Local authorities, for example, have the power to specify chimney heights for specific industrial processes and more stringent design standards are now being considered for car engines to reduce carbon dioxide emissions to the atmosphere.

iii) Prohibit certain activities

This response can relate to individual substances or can be used to restrict new industrial, commercial and residential developments in certain environmentally sensitive areas. For example, under the *Town and Country Planning (Assessments of Environmental Effects) Regulations* introduced in July 1988, demand is made for an *Environmental Impact Statement* from developers which should identify the impact of any development upon

'. . . human beings, flora, fauna, soil, air, water, climate, the landscape and cultural heritage.'

It is clear that both ambient and performance standards are mostly relevant to cases of point source pollution: these criteria are much more difficult to establish in relation to non-point pollution sources.

iv) Threshold Limits

The idea of *Threshold Limits* is one which has also been used in the setting of standards for pollution control. They have been used by the World Health Organisation (WHO) since 1970 and 1972 for setting water and air quality thresholds respectively and are constantly under revision (Table 1.6). These standards have been used by the EC in setting drinking water quality criteria which are enforceable in law. Although, as we saw earlier, our knowledge of the dose/response relationship is limited and reservations exist about their accuracy, they remain an important basis for setting standards.

Table 1.6 Selected drinking water standards as laid down by the European Community Directive of 1980

Parameter	Unit	Guide value	Max. value
a) Organoleptic parameters			
Colour	mg/l Pl	1	20
Turbidity	mg/l SiO_2	1	10
Odour	dil. factor	0	2–3
Taste	dil. factor	0	2–3
b) Physical/chemical parameters			
Temperature	°C	12	25
pH-value		6.5–8.5	9.5
Conductivity	µS	400	
Aluminium	mg/l	0.05	0.2
Dissolved oxygen	mg/l O_2	(at least 75% saturation)	
c) Unwanted parameters			
Nitrate	mg/l NO_3	25	50
Nitrite	mg/l NO_2	0.0	0.1
Copper	µg/l Cu	100	
Zinc	µg/l Zn	100	
Phosphorus	µg/l P_2O_5	400	5000

v) Standards in the workplace

In the UK, as in many other countries, pollution standards are applied to the work environment. For example, factory air pollution standards are based upon *Threshold Limit Values* which are defined as the highest safe dose. This type of standard is also used by the National Radiological Protection Board (NRPB) in order to ensure the safety of employees in the nuclear industry who must wear special film badges and be subject to regular health checks (Table 1.7).

Table 1.7 An example of the dose limits for workers in the nuclear industry

---

SCHEDULE 1
DOSE LIMITS
PART I
DOSE LIMITS FOR THE WHOLE BODY

1. The dose limit for the whole body resulting from exposure to the whole or part of the body, being the sum of the following dose quantities resulting from exposure to ionising radiation, namely the effective dose equivalent from external radiation and the committed effective dose equivalent from that year's intake of radionuclides, shall in any calendar year be:

(a) for employees aged 18 years or over,   50 mSv;
(b) for trainees aged under 18 years,   15 mSv;
(c) for any other person,   5 mSv.

3.3 Public participation

Public attitudes are becoming increasingly effective in influencing government decisions in the field of pollution control. Here we will briefly examine attitudes of the general public as well as managers.

i) Public perception and attitudes

The role of public perceptions, attitudes and responses is important in forcing the pace of pollution control. Very often, an incident will be brought to the attention of the public through the media. Subsequent public pressure may speed up legislation or action. In perception studies, this phenomenon is known as an *Issue Attention Cycle*. For example, in 1964 the Department of Housing and Local Government were aware of the illegal disposal of toxic waste and set up a committee to investigate it. In 1971 (seven years later) newspaper reports identified the fact that bonuses were being paid to lorry drivers for illegally dumping waste materials (in this case drums of cyanide). The law, following a major

public outcry, was modified in 1972 under the *Deposit of Poisonous Wastes Act* (1972).

Similar public pressures arose as a result of media coverage of the import of PCBs from Canada in 1989. These were to be treated at the ReChem plant in Pontypool. However, a local action group and the organisation *Greenpeace* brought widespread media attention to the import of waste into the UK. Further pressure was brought to bear on the government by dock workers refusing to handle the cargo and the waste material was eventually returned to Canada!

National and international pressure groups have had an important impact on many pollution issues, from waste treatment and disposal, through acid rain and water quality standards. In 1989, there were 4 major national and international pressure groups (Table 1.8) involved in a variety of ways but especially in influencing public awareness of environmental issues.

Table 1.8 The growth of international pressure groups concerned with environmental issues

Name	Membership	Income £	Year founded
Greenpeace	265 000	4 000 000	1971
Friends of the Earth	100 000	1 685 000	1971
Green Party*	13 000	180 000	1985
Ark	9 000	?	1988

*Evolved from the Ecology Party and People Party.

ii) Management attitudes

Perception by those individuals responsible for management is also important. For example, a recent study in Vancouver suggested that engineers were more concerned with social problems and urban growth, responding to pollution problems by means of improved water treatment facilities. In the same study, public health officials were more concerned with controlling pollution at source. Both groups argued strongly that the public were insufficiently well informed to participate in decision making processes in relation to pollution control!

The relationship between pollution and public perception is complex, and an attempt to show the linkages between the problem and its perception will be given in Part II.

3.4 National government and European Community involvement

i) Government regulation and control

In the UK, many government ministries are responsible for pollution control. Overall coordinating responsibility lies with the Secretary of State for the Environment who is assisted by the Environment Protection and Water Engineering Command.

In addition to national government being responsible for establishing an administrational framework for environmental quality, it is also responsible for establishing, through a variety of agencies, a data base containing information on environmental pollution. Many of these government sources will be discussed in Part III when examining sources of secondary data. Most monitoring is undertaken nationally, and an example is given of the distribution of river monitoring stations in the UK in Figure 1.20.

ii) The European Community

In the European Community, the *Council of Ministers*, appointed by member states, are responsible for making legislation. The Council is supported by a large civil service, the *European Commission*, which draws up proposals for its consideration and for the European Parliament.

The Commission works on the following types of action which, once agreed unanimously by the Council of Ministers, is binding on all member states.

1. *Regulations*, which are laws enforced directly by the EC.
2. *Directives*, which are binding agreements on all member states but are applied by National Government not directly by the EC.
3. *Decisions*, which are binding agreements not necessarily related to all member states.
4. *Recommendations*, which have no force in law.

In October 1972, member countries agreed that there should be a Community Environment Programme, which established five objectives.

1. Abolish harmful effects of pollution.
2. Manage a balanced ecology.
3. Improve the quality of life at work and elsewhere.
4. Deal with problems of urbanisation.
5. Cooperate with states outside the EC.

One of the principal aims was to establish environmental quality objectives for all major pollutants using the dose/response relationships described earlier.

Even though regulations and directives are agreed by the Council of Ministers, many instances exist of governments failing to comply. For example, the UK government failed to meet the EC 1980 directive on drinking water quality standards with respect to nitrate levels, arguing that the levels met average quality objectives but occasionally exceeded the limits at certain times of the year. Despite successful application for *derogations* (a temporary non-compliance with an EC directive) the EC threatened to take the UK government to court for persistent non-compliance in water supplies. Following appeals in September 1989, the EC confirmed that it would take the UK to the European Court. The outcome is not known at the time of writing.

Undoubtedly, the Environment Programme has caused disagreement amongst member states, especially over the use of different types of standard. Nevertheless, the main role of the EC has been to harmonise policies for the mutual benefit of member states and to this end has brought into force a number of directives dealing with air, water, marine and factory pollution.

3.5 The economics of pollution control

It is often thought desirable to balance the costs and benefits of alternative methods for controlling pollution and a number of alternative strategies are available.

i) Cost-benefit and environmental impact analysis

Cost-benefit analysis attempts to put a monetary value on pollution. It commonly divides the problem into two parts. First, an assessment is made of the benefits of permitting a particular discharge or allowing a particular development to take place. For example, the development of a new road in an area might decrease journey to work time and reduce the number of accidents which occured on a particular route. However, on the negative side may be the disturbance to the environment, and local increases in noise and lead levels along the new road. Cost-benefit analysis attempts to balance these two sides. It

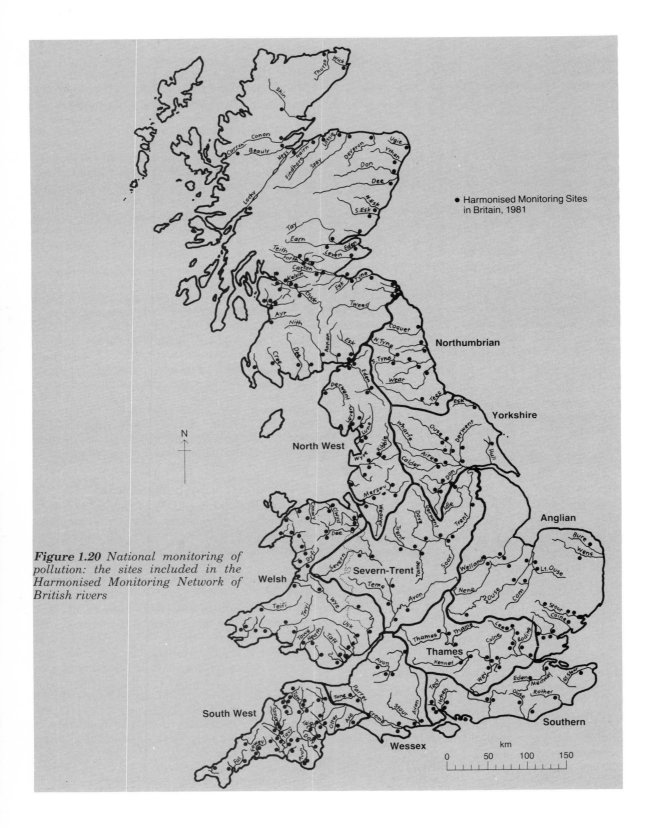

Figure 1.20 *National monitoring of pollution: the sites included in the Harmonised Monitoring Network of British rivers*

● Harmonised Monitoring Sites in Britain, 1981

was used in the UK following the London smogs of 1952 when the *Beaver Committee* tried to assess the economic benefits and disadvantages of air pollution prior to the *Clean Air Act*. However, as with all cost-benefit analyses, certain components are difficult to quantify, and therefore aesthetic damage to monuments, impaired recreational pleasure and cost of suffering from those afflicted with bronchial disorders were not measured.

Other strategies are now widely used as an alternative to cost-benefit analysis. For example, the use of *Environmental Impact Assessments* (EIAs), especially for new industrial and commercial development, is based upon a number of techniques which try to examine the impact of a particular planned development on all aspects of the environment. As seen on page 25, an Environmental Impact Statement is now demanded by law before new developments can take place.

ii) Regulation by taxation and fines

Governments may try to modify industrial behaviour based on purely economic principles, for example by imposing fines, by introducing tax incentives or offering assistance with particular problems. Fines or additional taxes may be levied if discharges to the environment exceed an agreed or specified level. This may encourage an industry to improve the manufacturing or pollution control technology because they will try to minimise taxes or fines. The latter were also used

by Regional Water Authorities in response to reported pollution incidents (Table 1.9), but because of the legal costs involved represent only a small proportion of the number of incidents reported (Table 1.2).

Similar principles of taxation incentive and the use of *government subsidies* may be used to reduce general as well as point source pollution. For example, the 1952 and 1968 *Clean Air Acts* entitled householders to a 70 per cent grant towards the cost of installing smokeless fuel appliances

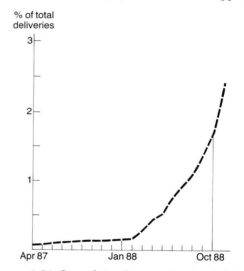

Figure 1.21 *Growth in the use of unleaded fuels at petrol stations*

Table 1.9 The number of prosecutions in the water industry by pollution type, 1987. This table can be compared directly with the data of Table 1.2a and b

Water Authority	Industrial			Farm	Sewage		Sewerage	Other	All causes
	Oil	Chemical	Other		Own	Other			
Anglian	1	2	6	23	—	—	—	—	32
Northumbrian	—	—	—	1	—	—	—	—	1
North West	4	← 15 →		25	—	—	—	4	48
Severn-Trent	—	1	12	24	—	—	—	—	37
Southern	←	2	→	6	—	—	—	—	8
South West	←	7	→	24	—	—	—	—	31
Thames	2	← 3 →		19	—	5	—	3	32
Welsh	5	4	25	50	—	1	—	—	85
Wessex	←	11	→	18	—	—	—	—	29
Yorkshire	3	7	12	13	—	—	—	1	36
England and Wales	←	122	→	203	—	6	—	8	339

when legislation forced them to change. Similarly, tax incentives were introduced in 1988 to use unleaded rather than leaded fuels in internal combustion engines by means of differential taxation. The response to this, plus a greater environmental awareness of the impact of lead on human health, has led to the trends shown in Figure 1.21.

An important question, of course, is who should ultimately be responsible for funding pollution control.

iii) The polluter pays?

We have seen above that policing of water pollution in the UK has led to few prosecutions. In 1973, however, member states of the EC officially adopted the principle that

> 'he who creates pollution should be financially responsible for controlling it.'

This principle was not accepted, however, by the EC Commission since it implies that those who can afford to pollute are given the right to do so irrespective of environmental or health risks involved. However, following the establishment of the National Rivers Authority in 1989, a proposal to set the cost of an industrial discharge licence in direct proportion to the amount of pollution caused was under consideration.

An alternative to this strategy is to pass the cost of pollution onto the consumer. This approach has already been implemented in the UK with the tax incentives for lead-free petrol as shown above, but may be extended to other areas of pollution control on consumer products. For example, in 1989, the UK government was considering additional Value Added Tax (VAT) to be used for consumer products which create pollution. With privatisation of the UK water industry, it has also been made clear by the UK government that, in order to meet EC directives on water pollution, much of the cost of water quality improvement will be passed on to the consumer and will not be directly funded by national government.

Implementation of fines, incentives or other economic controls on industry, as well as enforcing legislation, demands that some form of policing is implemented in the form of environmental monitoring. To this end, organisations such as the Alkali Inspectorate and the National Rivers Authority are responsible for policing air and river water quality respectively.

3.6 International problems of pollution control

Over the last three decades, there has been an increase in the awareness of, and response to, international problems of pollution. A number of environmental issues are important at this level and the following brief examples are given to highlight some of the problems and principles involved.

Problems may derive from continuous emissions, such as sulphur dioxide from power stations, or from accidental spillages, especially in international waters. A number of international organisations have attempted to establish guidelines on these issues. Of particular importance is the United Nations which, in a 1972 Conference on Human Rights, established two important principles

> Nations . . . (have) . . . the responsibility to ensure that activities within their jurisdiction or control do not cause damage to the environment of other states . . .

> States shall cooperate to develop further the international law regarding liability and compensation for victims of pollution and other environmental damage caused by activities within their jurisdiction.

Recently, international agreements have been developed in relation to the acid rain problem in Europe. The impetus was provided by a meeting of international experts at a meeting in Stockholm in 1982 who identified the nature and extent of the problem. A ministerial meeting at the same conference ratified the conclusions of the experts and set the scene for an international reduction in sulphur dioxide emissions by 1993. Disagreement existed on the timescale of reductions although, by April 1985, 21 countries acceded to the Norwegian demand of a 30 per cent reduction (*The 30% Club*) in sulphur dioxide levels by 1993. Neither France, the UK nor the USA agreed to this timetable.

Undoubtedly, international agreements and the harmonisation of international standards will, in the long term, improve environmental quality.

Part II
CASE STUDIES

1 INTRODUCTION

Two case studies are given in this section to illustrate some of the issues discussed in Part I. These case studies will examine first, a *diffuse* pollutant from agriculture, with reference to the Jersey nitrate problem, and secondly, a *point source* of pollution, with reference to the Chernobyl nuclear accident.

2 THE JERSEY NITRATE PROBLEM

2.1 Introduction

As we saw in Part I, nitrate levels in both surface water and groundwater in the UK have increased rapidly over the last 20 years, at a rate often more than 2 per cent per year. The quality of water in many cases reflects land use and farm management and decisions taken by individual farmers. However, farmers do not act in isolation because their decisions are influenced by the general public, agricultural, health and water management organisations and, of course, the media.

2.2 The problem

The island of Jersey has limited sources of fresh water supplies, most of which contain high levels of nitrate. Public water supplies come from three main sources.

1. In the south of the island, especially around St. Helier, a mains water supply is provided by an independent public water supply company, the Jersey New Water Works Company (JNWC). Most public water supplies are obtained from catchments and collected in small reservoirs (Figure 2.1).
2. A desalination plant (distilling fresh water from sea water) was built at La Rosiere in 1970 to provide extra supplies to the urban areas at times of shortage, but is expensive to operate. When in use, the water is added to reservoirs and distributed through mains supplies.
3. In rural areas, (mainly in the north of the island) most farmers and households are supplied from groundwater. Many farms have their own boreholes and no quality control is exercised on these remote sources.

Although most river valleys contain small reservoirs, the JNWC identified potential shortfalls as water demand was predicted to increase in the future. This led to a range of plans to build a new reservoir in the Queen's Valley and increase the storage capacity of other reservoirs.

However, in addition to the problem of water shortage, water quality in many of the water supply catchments is poor because of the presence of high nitrate levels.

Figure 2.2 shows the nitrate content of drinking water in Jersey from mains supplies. At worst, the EC drinking water standard was exceeded 75 per cent of the time (i.e. 274 days in a year), whilst at best this limit was only exceeded 18 per cent of the time (i.e. 66 days of the year) in 1984. Maximum concentrations in borehole supplies to the north of the island reach 45 mg l^{-1} NO_3-N (milligrams of nitrogen as nitrate per litre of water) and the EC limit is exceeded more than 60 per cent of the time.

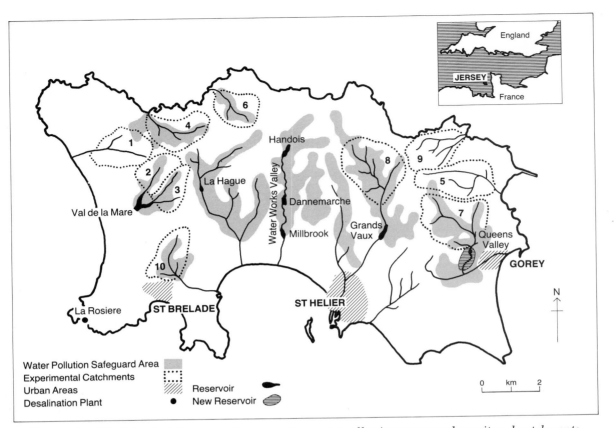

Figure 2.1 *The island of Jersey: main reservoirs, water collecting areas and monitored catchments*

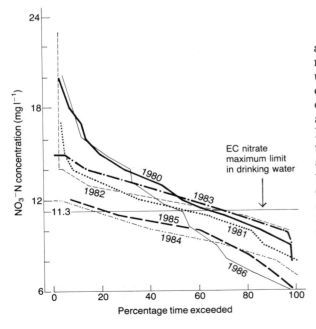

Data for nitrate levels in ten catchments are available over a ten month period. The catchments are shown in Figure 2.1 and details of land utilisation and summary statistics for nitrate concentrations are given in Table 2.1. From these data we can see that the highest concentrations are found in those catchments that devote the largest percentage of their area to intensive cultivation (here defined as the area under potatoes and cauliflowers). In particular, catchment C2, with 80 per cent of its area under potatoes and cauliflowers, has the highest concentrations of around 40 mg l^{-1} NO$_3$–N; this falls to only around 18 mg l^{-1} in C10, where less than a quarter of the catchment is under intense cultivation.

Figure 2.2 *Nitrate exceedence curves for mains water supplies*

Table 2.1 Land use and water quality characteristics of the 10 Jersey catchments

| Catchment | Name | Size (ha) | Area under (%) | | | | | Nitrate concentrations (NO_3^-N) (mgl^{-1}) | | | |
			Potatoes	Cauli-flower	Other crops	Grass	Wood-land	Min.	Max.	Mean	Standard deviation
C1	L'Etacq	145	50	10	13	7	5	5.0	30.0	13.0	9.30
C2	Val de la Mare 1	210	72	8	1	3	6	4.0	38.0	14.0	8.30
C3	Val de la Mare 2	190	39	11	4	26	10	6.0	18.0	12.0	4.39
C4	Greve de Lacq	215	32	18	8	12	10	4.5	36.0	11.5	7.10
C5	St Catherines	210	52	16	3	12	10	8.0	18.0	12.0	4.82
C6	Les Mourier	184	46	14	15	14	6	6.5	25.0	10.0	3.47
C7	Queens Valley	240	18	7	5	53	9	5.5	17.0	9.0	4.03
C8	St Saviour	260	32	8	7	30	8	5.0	18.0	10.0	3.02
C9	Rozel Bay	163	48	4	5	15	20	6.0	17.0	10.5	3.55
C10	St Brelade	185	18	6	2	14	14	5.0	18.0	10.0	3.60

These data and analyses point to a significant association between drinking water quality, river and borehole nitrate levels and the area of land under intensive cultivation.

2.3 Jersey agriculture

Fifty-six per cent of the island is under agriculture. Land ownership and farm size data for 1977–1986 are given in Table 2.2. Since many farmers produce two crops a year from the same field, the total cropped area in 1986 amounted to 9766 ha. Just over half of this area was utilised for outdoor vegetables and fruit, of which 50 per cent was devoted to potato production.

Maximum applications of nitrogen fertiliser for the decade 1977–1986 were 189 kg N ha^{-1} yr^{-1} (kilograms of nitrogen per hectare per year). A questionnaire survey of 46 farmers in 1986 showed that 59 per cent of them applied nitrogen twice a year and 41 per cent three times a year. Many farmers used more than the maximum recommended levels for various crops and a small proportion of farmers applied about twice the requirement because they thought that crop yields would be higher if they used more fertiliser (Table 2.3). These applications are much higher than in many areas of Europe.

Table 2.2 The agricultural structure of Jersey, 1977–86

	1977	1981	1986
Land area (ha)			
Owned	2542	2639	2637
Rented	4239	4197	3965
Total	6781	6836	6602
Number of holdings (by size)			
<1.8 ha	245	232	216
1.9–4.5 ha	160	128	101
4.6–9.0 ha	218	184	125
9.1–13.5 ha	126	104	90
13.6–18.0 ha	68	75	62
>18 ha	73	89	101
Total No.	890	812	695
Average farm size (ha)	7.6	8.4	9.5

Source: States of Jersey Agricultural Statistics for the years 1977–86. Department of Agriculture and Fisheries, St Helier.

Table 2.3 Fertiliser application practice amongst interviewed farmers

Crop	Amount applied (kg ha^{-1} yr^{-1})	Farmers applying (per cent)
Potatoes	165–172[a]	32
	220–274	36
	275–302	28
	>302	4
Cauliflowers	90–100[a]	45
	110–130	39
	140–150	16

[a]Optimum application given by States of Jersey Agricultural Department.

2.4 Perception of the nitrate problem

Many Jersey farmers do not think themselves responsible for the nitrate pollution problem. Indeed, they are far more concerned about their farming enterprise. The 46 farmers interviewed in relation to nitrogen application rates were asked what they considered to be the major problem confronting them. Most identified competition from other countries and lack of support from the Jersey States (Jersey's parliament) as their most important problems today. Environmental issues were not mentioned by any of the farmers questioned!

Over 90 per cent of farmers were aware of nitrate pollution, believing it to be a recent problem, but only 52 per cent considered pollution to be a serious issue. The younger farmers were far more aware of the problem than the older farmers.

Although there is evidence of farmer awareness, only 11 per cent were prepared to limit fertiliser applications if requested; the majority were more concerned with potential declines in crop yield if they stopped using such high quantities.

Fifty-eight members of the public were interviewed at the same time in a separate questionnaire survey of urban and rural areas. Only 29 per cent identified nitrate pollution as a major issue, of which 88 per cent lived in rural areas and received borehole water.

Having been shown the data of Figure 2.2, the interviewees were asked who they thought was responsible for the problem. Sixty-nine per cent

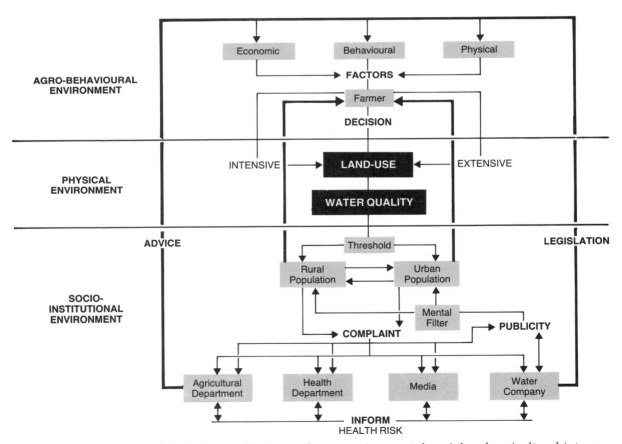

Figure 2.3 *A general model of nitrate pollution on Jersey: environmental, social and agricultural interactions*

blamed farmers and only 9 per cent blamed the JNWC. Fifty-seven per cent of respondents felt that there should be some control over the use of fertilisers.

Information on these local environmental issues was mainly obtained from newspapers and a local pressure group *Concern*. Few knew of the health effects of nitrates and only one respondent took action by purchasing bottled water.

2.5 Institutional attitudes

Interviews with the JNWC, the Agricultural Department, the Public Health Department and with the Planning Department of the Jersey States showed that they are all aware of the nitrate problem. *Water Pollution Safeguard Areas* around water supply catchments have been identified where fertiliser applications should be limited (Figure 2.1). However, the JNWC has little power to enforce standards of agricultural practice in its water catchment areas and has responded to the problem with the construction of a new reservoir in the Queen's Valley (Figure 2.1). The better quality water which will be derived from this source may in future improve the quality of water supplied to urban areas.

Although information and restrictions are issued to farmers, these are mostly ignored. Public information, however, is less forthcoming. The link between the Public Health Department and members of the public is non-existent, despite the fact that the Department has a legal obligation to inform members of the public that their water supply contains nitrate at unacceptable levels and that young children in particular should be given bottled water.

2.6 Conclusions

The nitrate problem is complex, and involves decisions taken both by farmers and by institutions responsible for controlling pollution. An attempt to simplify the problem is made in the general model of the Jersey nitrate issue in Figure 2.3. This model shows that the physical relationship between land use and water quality is influenced by farmers behaviour on the one hand and a group of interrelated factors of a social and governmental nature on the other hand.

This study also shows that understanding of the problem requires information not only on the problem itself but also on factors which may provide some indication of the best ways to solve it.

3   THE CHERNOBYL NUCLEAR ACCIDENT

3.1 Introduction

In Part I, we examined a range of pollutant types and looked at sources of both artificial and natural radiations. These issues, along with those relating to point source pollution and risk assessment, are of relevance here. Section 2.5 in Part I provided some predictions regarding the likelihood of a nuclear accident. In April 1986, the unthinkable happened!

Chernobyl is a small town in the Soviet Union standing on the banks of the Prypiat River near its confluence with the Rivers Dneiper and Uzh in the northern Ukraine (Figure 2.5). The word Chernobyl, somewhat ironically, translates into English as Wormwood (a small perennial herb

with bitter qualities). The events which occurred in this town on Saturday 26th April 1986 will long be remembered as one of the worst environmental disasters associated with the effects of human activity on the environment and some may even argue that a biblical prophecy has been realised.

And the name of the star is called Wormwood
and the third part of the waters became Wormwood
and many men died of the waters
because they were made bitter.

Revelations Ch8 v11.

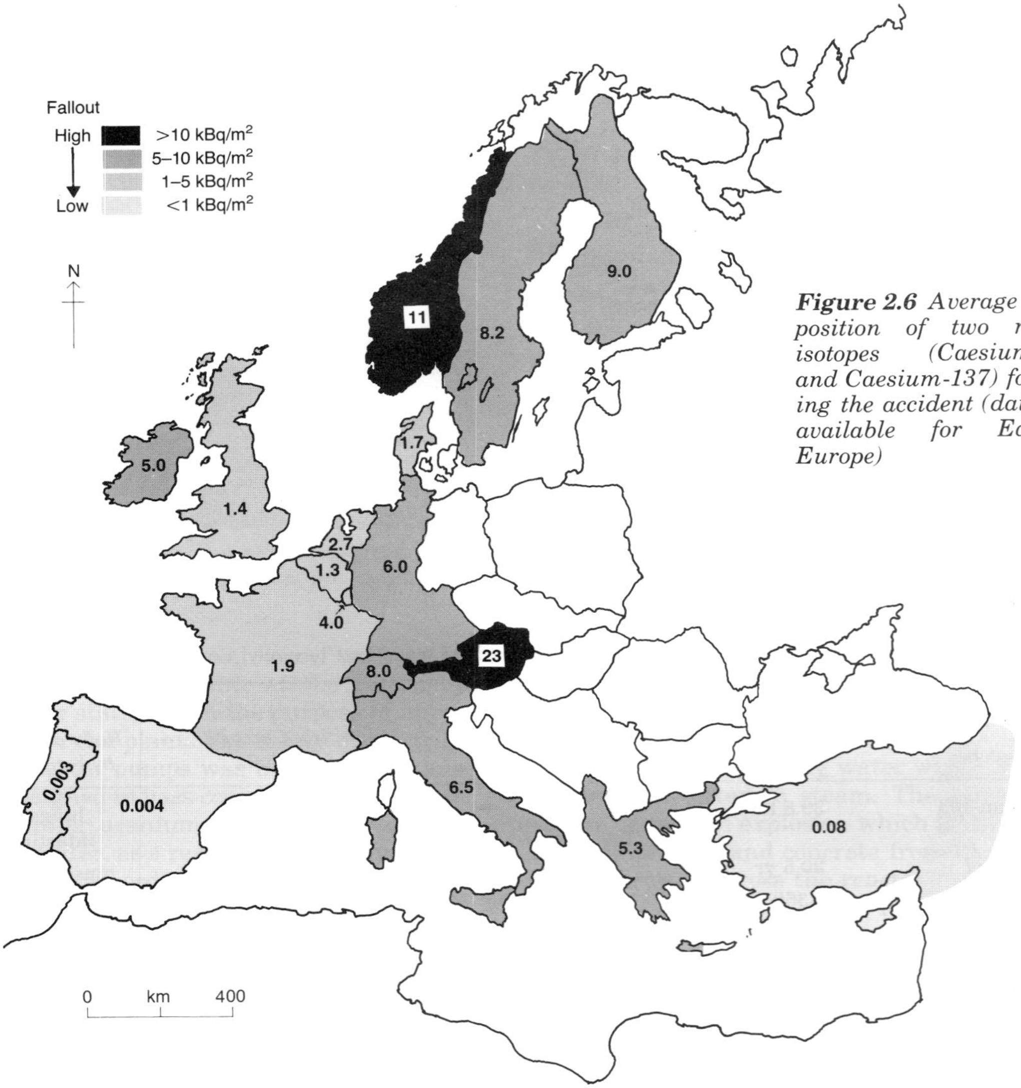
Fallout
High
Low
>10 kBq/m²
5–10 kBq/m²
1–5 kBq/m²
<1 kBq/m²
N
11
8.2
9.0
5.0
1.4
1.7
2.7
1.3
6.0
4.0
1.9
8.0
23
0.003
0.004
6.5
5.3
0.08
0 km 400

Figure 2.6 *Average deposition of two radioisotopes (Caesium-134 and Caesium-137) following the accident (data not available for Eastern Europe)*

er the UK. It moved over the North Sea and then recrossed parts of the UK. The general pattern of dispersal is shown in Figure 2.5.

Although the radioactive cloud passed over most of North West Europe, not all regions received an equal amount of pollution added to soils, rivers and lakes. This is because the amount deposited on the ground depended on the pattern of rainfall as the cloud passed over different countries. Average values of deposited radioactive Caesium (Caesium-137 and Caesium-134) in member countries of the OECD (Organisation for Economic Cooperation and Development) show high levels in Scandinavia, West Germany, Austria, Switzerland, Italy and Greece. Low levels were recorded in Turkey, Spain and Portugal and intermediate levels in the UK, Eire, Denmark, the Netherlands, Belgium and France (Figure 2.6). A detailed examination of radioactive fallout in the UK shows a pattern similar to

Figure 2.7 *Deposition of Caesium-137 in the UK (Bq/m²)*

annual average rainfall because the radiation in the cloud was washed out of the atmosphere by falling rain. High levels were recorded in North Central Scotland, Galloway, Cumbria and North Wales. The levels recorded here were more than 100 times the levels over Central, Southern and South West England (Figure 2.7).

Analysis of milk products and animals in many of these high fallout areas revealed severe radiation contamination in a range of human foodstuffs and radiation levels well above the nationally approved safety limits. The immediate government response was to impose restrictions on the movement and sale of animals and animal products for human consumption in many of these areas. Some of these restrictions had not been lifted in 1989, three years after the accident! A secondary response in 1987 was to improve radiation monitoring and early warning in the UK. The responsibility for such monitoring now lies with local government who must undertake routine monitoring of foodstuffs and be able to provide an emergency monitoring system if another accident should occur.

3.4 Environmental impacts

Since 1986, several national and international studies have been undertaken to monitor the effects of the Chernobyl accident. For example, in one of the most polluted areas of Cumbria, increases in the radioactivity of lake waters were recorded (Figure 2.8). Similar increases in the radioactivity of brown trout have also been found in these lakes (Figure 2.8). High levels of Caesium-134 which is known to have come from the Chernobyl accident only are to be found in soils, vegetation and even in the sediments accumulating at the bottom of lakes and reservoirs. As yet, however, we know little about the likely fate and future movements of radio-isotopes in the natural environment in order to predict what future problems we may face.

3.5 Conclusions

We may learn much in general from this single incident, and the main conclusions are presented in summary form below.

1. Safety regulations and operating practices are subject to human error which makes risk assessment in any industry (but particularly the nuclear industry) difficult.
2. An accident in a relatively small power plant may have international repercussions resulting from dispersal of the radioactive cloud. Indeed the OECD member states held their own enquiry into nuclear safety following the accident and recommended changes in operating practices for all nuclear power stations.
3. Rapid dispersal may pose not only a health risk but also a risk to the economy and environment. The latter is still not fully understood despite a large number of studies dealing with environmental radioactivity.

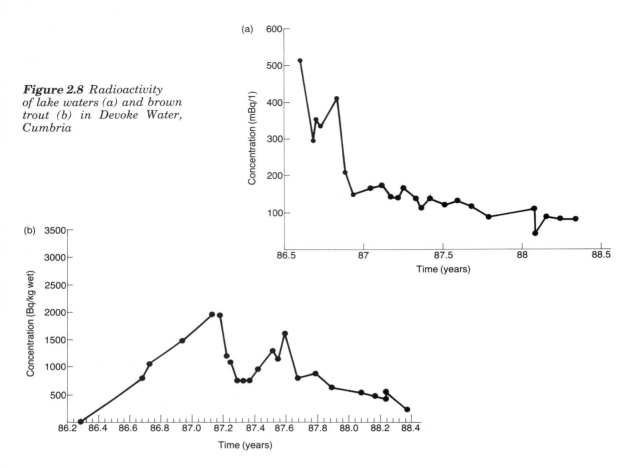

Figure 2.8 *Radioactivity of lake waters (a) and brown trout (b) in Devoke Water, Cumbria*

Use of nuclear power is often the subject of political discussion and decision making in the light of public pressures, economic and environmental factors. Undoubtedly, the Chernobyl accident leaves a conflict of interest. Western societies consume energy, much generated by nuclear power (Table 2.5). If we produce it from fossil fuel, we risk further problems from acid rain and carbon dioxide. If we produce it from nuclear power, we run the risk of a second Chernobyl and the problem of how to decommission old power stations. At the time of writing, the UK government has withdrawn the nuclear power industry from its proposals for privatisation due to the economics of shutting down old stations. We have yet to see whether or not new stations will be built in the future.

Table 2.5 The percentage of power generated in nuclear power stations in the EC, 1983 and 1985

Region	% of total electricity output	
	1983	*1985*
EC (12)	21.0	30.7
W. Germany	17.8	31.2
France	48.3	64.8
Italy	3.1	3.8
Netherlands	5.9	6.1
Belgium	45.7	59.8
Luxembourg	0	0
UK	16.9	19.3
Ireland	0	0
Denmark	0	0
Greece	0	0
Spain	9.1	22.0
Portugal	0	0

1 INTRODUCTION

Analysis of pollution problems can make use of both *primary* and *secondary* data. *Primary data* are those that we collect using our own sampling methods in the field and analytical methods in the laboratory. *Secondary data* are those collected by another agency but which we can use to analyse some aspect of pollution in a way that we could not do by setting up our own sampling scheme. In addition to using primary and secondary data to study pollution, we can also make use of *back-of-envelope* calculations to examine some aspects of the problem. Here we can make use of general observations to explore some aspects of pollution without spending a long time collecting either primary or secondary data.

Part III is divided into three sections: first, we will look at back-of-envelope calculations, secondly, primary data collection exercises, and finally we will examine secondary data sources and how they might be analysed.

a Primary data collection: measuring the acidity of a river

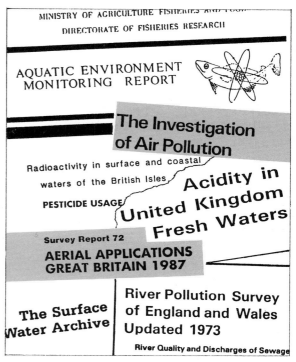

b Secondary data sources: some of the official government publications and sources of information available for reference

Figure 3.1 *Primary and secondary data*

2 BACK-OF-ENVELOPE CALCULATIONS

Calculations of this type are important for getting a basic understanding of pollution problems. There are many environmental problems which can be tackled using this approach, but the problem given here deals with phosphorus pollution from agriculture and sewage.

2.1 Phosphorus pollution

You have been called in as an expert to solve a problem concerning the pollution of a small lake. The lake was once of good quality, with plentiful fishing and water sports activities. It has now become *eutrophic* (see Part I). This has happened because there is too much phosphorus (P) entering the lake. Your first task is to try and establish whether most of the P comes from a sewage works or from cultivated land because of high fertiliser use and high rates of soil erosion. You have been given the following brief description of the lake and its catchment.

The lake receives water from a 250 ha drainage basin which is currently cultivated with cereals (wheat). There is also a sewage works at the side of the lake serving a small village with a population of 2000 people. (On average, each person produces 200 litres of effluent at the sewage works per day.) Rainfall for the area is 800 mm yr^{-1} and brings in 0.1 kg ha^{-1} of P. Runoff in the river is 450 mm yr^{-1}. Soil erosion rates for the area are 400 kg ha^{-1}. The data in Table 3.1 are also provided.

Table 3.1. Statistics on phosphorus (P) in soil and water

Phosphorus concentration in:		
Soils (g kg^{-1})	River water (mg l^{-1})	Sewage effluent (mg l^{-1})
2.0	.012	5

g kg^{-1} = grams per kilogram of soil (g/kg)
mg l^{-1} = milligrams per litre of water (mg/l)

1. On the basis of the information given above, draw a flow diagram using proportional line symbols to show where most of the P in the lake comes from.

2. Compare the input of P to the lake with the amount that would reach the lake from an undisturbed forested basin as shown in the worked example below.

3. Describe your findings, and explain how you think the problem should be tackled.

4. You have just discovered that a new sewage treatment process can be fitted to the sewage works. It will reduce the average concentration of P in the sewage outfall to 0.1 mg l^{-1}. What effect will this have on the amount of P reaching the lake?

Worked example

We can illustrate how to tackle the problem with reference to a natural forested drainage basin of exactly the same size in the local area which also drains into a lake. We know that this catchment is slightly different. The soils only contain 0.5 g kg^{-1} of P, that there is less runoff (only 380 mm), that average P concentrations in runoff are low (0.005 mg l^{-1}) and that soil erosion rates are also low (100 kg ha^{-1}). P inputs in rainfall are the same.

We can approach this problem in a simple and logical way.

a) Calculate the P input in rainfall. For the catchment, the total input is 0.1 kg ha^{-1}. Catchment area is 250 ha and the total input is therefore $250 \times 0.1 = 25$ kg.

b) Calculate the P output in solution reaching the lake.

Area = 250 ha (1 ha = 100 m $\times$ 100 m)
Runoff = 380 mm (0.38 m)
P conc. = 0.005 mg l^{-1}
= 0.005 $\times$ 1000 mg m^3 = 5 mg m^3

Volume of runoff = area $\times$ depth (always use the same units!). Therefore, runoff (R, in m^3) is

R = 250 $\times$ 100 $\times$ 100 $\times$ 0.38 = 950 000 m^3

P conc. = 5 mg m^3

Therefore, total P = 950 000 $\times$ 5 mg
= 4750 g
= 4.75 kg

The total amount of P reaching the lake in solution is 4.75 kg per year from an input in solution of 25 kg per year.

c) Calculate the amount of P reaching the lake with soil erosion.

Soil erosion   = 100 kg ha^{-1}
P conc.   = 0.5 g kg^{-1} soil.
For each ha of catchment, P loss
    = 100 × 0.5 g
    = 50 g
    = .05 kg
Area is 250 ha, therefore the total loss is
    250 × .05 = 12.5 kg

On the basis of these calculations, we can contruct a proportional line diagram (Figure 3.2) to show the input and output of P to a lake from a forested catchment. Use the same methods to calculate the input of P to the lake from the sewage works and from the dissolved and sediment loads reaching the lake from the cultivated catchment.

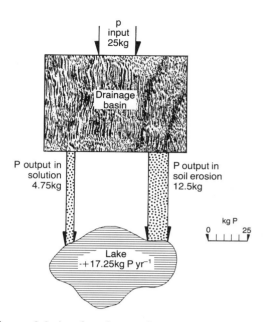

Figure 3.2 A phosphorus budget for a forested drainage basin

3   PRIMARY DATA

Exercises making use of primary data can be many and varied. The following three exercises assume that attention has been given to the location of sampling sites and setting up of a good theory to test (see Matthews and Foster, 1989).

3.1 Air pollution and acid rain

In addition to the secondary information collected from a range of government sources (see section 4 on page 46), you may decide to collect your own acid rain and air pollution data.

At a single site, you could use the following basic equipment.

Acid rain collector
1 pole 1.75 m long or length of wood of 25 × 25 mm cross-section
2 strong elastic bands
1 plastic 1000 ml bottle covered with a dark plastic bag
1 rubber bung
1 piece of glass wool

Atmospheric dust fallout collector
1 pole or length of timber 25 × 25 mm
1 piece of wood, 25 × 10 cm, 5 mm thick
1 length of sticky-backed fablon

The construction of these two simple pieces of field equipment is shown in Figure 3.3.

a)

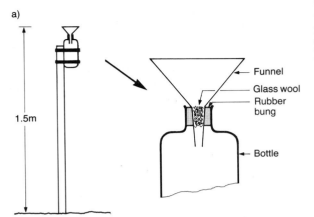

a *A simple funnel collector for acid rain measurement*

b)

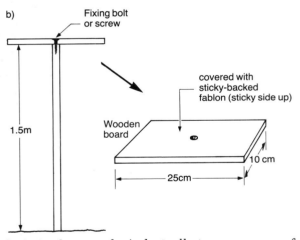

b *A simple atmospheric dust collector over an area of 250 cm²*

Figure 3.3 *Atmospheric pollution monitoring*

Measurement of pH can be made in a number of ways depending on the availability of equipment. At the simplest, a range of pH sensitive indicator papers are commercially available. Some of these are sensitive to very small changes in pH which allow accurate estimation to within around 0.2 pH units. If available, however, a pH meter will give greater accuracy and precision. Make sure that the collectors are located in open sites away from hedges, trees and tall buildings.

Water samples from the collector should be emptied weekly, although it is quite acceptable to collect rainfall over much shorter time periods (e.g. every day or even every hour during a heavy rainstorm). pH should be measured as soon as possible after collection; within a maximum time of 24 hours. If kept overnight, store the sample in a refrigerator but do not freeze the sample.

For the dust collector, the sticky backed fablon should be removed either monthly or weekly and an attempt made to estimate how much dust has fallen over the intervening period. In order to estimate the amount of dust, two methods might be used:

1. If a very accurate (to 0.001 g) balance is available, weigh the fablon (after drying over a radiator) before and after it is put out into the field and calculate the amount of dust collected.

weight before (B) − weight after (A) = dust weight (W)

dust fallout per m² is calculated from

$$W \times 4$$

because the sampling area is 0.25 m²

2. Where an accurate balance is not available, an alternative method is to place a 5 cm² grid drawn on thin tracing paper over the collected sample and estimate the amount of fablon (as a percentage) covered by dust particles. For your own area, devise a suitable scale. For example:

Class 1   ≤ 10%
Class 2   11–20%
Class 3   21–30%
Class 4   31–40%
Class 5   41–50%
Class 6   51–60%
Class 7   61–70%
Class 8   > 70%

These class intervals can be used to either map the spatial distribution of dust fallout for your own area or to examine changes through time at a single station.

The techniques described above may be used to examine changes in rainfall acidity and dust fallout over space or through time. There are a number of experiments which could be conducted using these simple methods such as:

1. Examine the short term changes in rainfall pH during a single rainstorm (e.g. every 30 min).

2. Examine the seasonal changes in rainfall pH based on monthly sampling (e.g. is pH lower in winter than summer?).

3. Examine the spatial variations in pH and dust fallout in an urban area (e.g. set up several stations in students' gardens across the city).

4. Compare dust fallout in relation to major roads (e.g. does fallout decrease with distance away from the road?).

5. Compare dust levels within and outside of buildings.

3.2 Freshwater pollution

Experiments designed to examine the pollution of freshwater bodies, i.e. rivers, lakes and canals, often requires access to sophisticated laboratory equipment. However, there are some simple measurements which can provide useful data relating to the pollution of fresh water.

i) The Secci disk

One useful measure, especially for lakes and canals, is the transparency of the water which will relate both to the amount of sediment in the water and to the productivity of the water body (see Part I). This may be measured using a Secci disk which can be constructed from a pole, between 1 and 2 m in length, with a white plastic disk of around 10 cm diameter fixed to one end (Figure 3.4). The disk is lowered into the water until it

can no longer be seen and the depth to which it has sunk is recorded.

ii) pH and temperature

Measuring pH using either of the methods given above will provide information on the acidity of the water. Temperature may be measured with a simple mercury thermometer. Remember that water temperatures will vary throughout the day and measurements should always be made at the same time of day.

iii) Nitrates

Similar indicator papers to those used for determining pH are now available for the determination of nitrate concentrations in water samples. These papers are both accurate and reliable for field testing of water samples.

iv) Species diversity

A simple measure of water quality is obtained by looking at invertebrate species in the river. If a sample net is available, sample the river for a 2 minute period over a fixed area of river bed (about 1 m^2). Examine the specimens collected in the net by eye and count how many different species of invertebrates you have caught. In general, the greater the number of species, the better quality the water.

v) Visual classification

The presence of rubbish, bricks, shopping trolleys etc. can be used to provide an index score of visual pollution as indicated in section 3.3 below.

A number of useful field investigations may be performed using the 5 measures briefly described above. For example, you could answer some of the following questions which may be relevant to your local area:

1. Does water pollution increase as a river flows through an urban area?

2. How does the water quality of urban and rural lakes change through time? (For example, over a year based on monthly sampling.)

3. What affect does agriculture have on water pollution? (For example, by comparing rivers draining forested areas with those draining fields.)

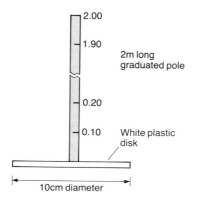

Figure 3.4 *A Secci disk for measuring water transparency in lakes, canals and rivers*

As indicated above, considerable thought should be given to designing the experiment and asking the right questions before measuring anything in the field.

3.3 Pollution of the land

The field techniques described above may be suitable for studying some aspects of pollution, but there are many other forms of pollution, such as noise and litter, which may be assessed and mapped in both the urban and rural environment. The most objective way of assessing a variety of pollutant types is to use a point score system, such as that given in Table 3.2. This point scoring system allows evaluation of traffic and industrial air pollution, litter, noise, the presence of landfill sites and the environmental impact of farmyards. This type of classification scheme was used to construct the map of pollution in Greater Manchester (Figure 1.17, page 21).

The area to be mapped should be divided into a number of regular areas, for example by using the 1 km² grid network of the Ordnance Survey. In each square, use the point score system for the 8 classes given in Table 3.2. These data may be used to map individual forms of pollution for the area or summed to give an aggregate pollution index for the grid square as a whole.

Similar methods may be used to assess the pollution of beaches and coasts, but the point scoring system of Table 3.2 will have to be mod-

ified in order to include other forms of pollutant, such as the presence or absence of sewage outfall pipes and oil on beaches.

Table 3.2 A point score system for assessing environmental pollution

			Score
1	Traffic (producing air pollution)	Heavy traffic	-4 to -5
		Medium traffic	-1 to -3
		Light traffic	0
2	Industrial air pollution	Heavy	-4 to -5
		Moderate	-1 to -3
		Light	0
3	Litter	Much litter	-4 to -5
		Some litter	-1 to -3
		Little litter	0
4	Noise	Difficult to talk	-4 to -5
		Reasonable to talk	-1 to -3
		Acceptable background	0
5	Fouling of pavements	Heavy	-4 to -5
		Occasional	-1 to -3
		No fouling	0
6	Landfill/ waste tips	Over 50% of area	-7 to -10
		10–50% of area	-2 to -6
		Less than 10% of area	0 to -1
7	Water pollution (If in Square) (Rivers and Lakes)	Heavily polluted	-4 to -5
		Moderately polluted	-1 to -3
		Little pollution	0
8	Farmyards/ silage clamps	Heavy pollution	-7 to -10
		Moderate pollution	-2 to -6
		Little pollution	0 to -1

4 SECONDARY DATA SOURCES AND ANALYSIS

A range of secondary data sources are available for investigating pollution (Table 3.3).

The following exercise is based upon data obtained from the Digest of Environmental Protection and Water Statistics and reproduced in Tables 1.2a and b and 1.9.

For Table 1.2a

1. Draw a bar graph for each Water Authority region to show the number of water pollution incidents in each of the eight years.
2. Draw a bar graph to show the number of pollution incidents for England and Wales as a whole for each of the eight years.

3. Describe the trends in the number of pollution incidents for England and Wales, and use the graphs from the individual Water Authority regions to identify where most of the increases in pollution incidents came from.

For Table 1.2b

1. On a map of Water Authority regions of England and Wales (trace the outline from Figure 1.20), draw ten circles with areas proportional to the total number of pollution incidents by all causes. (The radius of the circle should be proportional to the square root of the value.

The best scale for these data is obtained by dividing all values by 100 and taking the square root of the number. For example, for Anglian Water there were 1605 incidents. Dividing by 100 gives a value of 16.05, and the radius of the circle is the square root of this value, which is 4.01 units).

2. Use each circle to produce divided pie charts showing the percentage of pollution incidents in 1987 coming from industry, farms, sewage and other sources.
3. Comment on the regional variations in the number and type of pollution incidents shown.

For Table 1.9

1. The total number of prosecutions by all causes should form the basis for comparison with the number of incidents reported. This can be shown graphically by means of a choropleth map. Use a base map of Water Authority regions. Divide the data into class intervals representing the number of prosecutions. For example:

    Class 1   Less than 20
    Class 2   21 to 39
    Class 3   More than 40

2. Choose a shading density for each class interval (make the shading darker for higher values) and shade the map.
3. Compare the number of prosecutions with the number of reported incidents from your analysis of Table 1.2b.

4. Discuss the various alternative methods which might be used to reduce the number of water pollution incidents in England and Wales.

Table 3.3 Secondary data sources for pollution studies

All are published by HMSO unless otherwise stated.

1 General statistics
Regional Trends
Royal Commission on Environmental Pollution (Various)
Digest of Environmental Protection and Water Statistics

2 Air pollution
National Survey (Smoke and Sulphur Dioxide)
Health and Safety (Industrial Air Pollution)
Annual Report of the Chief Alkali Inspector (N. Ireland)
Transport Statistics, Great Britain

3 Water pollution
Freshwater Survey of England and Wales (various dates from 1970) (Volume 3 contains data on coastal pollution)
Digest of Welsh Statistics
Waterfacts
Annual Reports (Regional Water Authorities)
Aquatic Environment Monitoring Report

4 Other sources
Environmental Radioactivity Surveillance Programme (NRPB)
Radioactivity in Surface and Coastal Waters of the British Isles
Annual Report on Radioactive Discharges and Monitoring of the Environment.

SUGGESTED READING

Dawson, A.D. (1991) Climatic Change. Oxford University Press.

Goudie, A. (1981) The Human Impact. Blackwell.

Haynes, V. and M. Bojcun (1988) The Chernobyl Disaster. Hogarth Press.

Ilbery, B. (1991) Agricultural Change in the UK. Oxford University Press.

Matthews, M.H. (1991) British Inner Cities. Oxford University Press.

Matthews, M.H. and I.D.L. Foster (1989) Geographical Data: sources, presentation, and analysis. Oxford University Press.

McCormick, J. (1985) Acid Earth. Earthscan.

OECD (1986) Water pollution by fertilizers and Pesticides. OECD.

Royal Commission on Environmental Pollution (1984) Tenth Report. Tackling Pollution – Experience and Prospects. HMSO.

Sandbach, F. (1982) Principles of Pollution Control. Longman.

INDEX